SCOTT, FORESMAN AND COMPANY

EXPLORING MATHEMATICS ®

Problem Solving and Critical Thinking
Sourcebook

The Activities in this Sourcebook

One Activity Master, along with a Teacher Notes page, is provided for each lesson in the student text. There are four categories of thinking skills, each addressing a different area of mathematical reasoning. The four categories are Problem Solving, Critical Thinking, Visual Thinking, and Decision Making.

Contents

Pages

Correlation Chart

This correlation chart is an easy-to-use reference and index for the Activity Masters in this book. The Objective Numbers that are used for the Activity Masters are the same numbers that are used to identify the objectives in the Student Edition.

Key

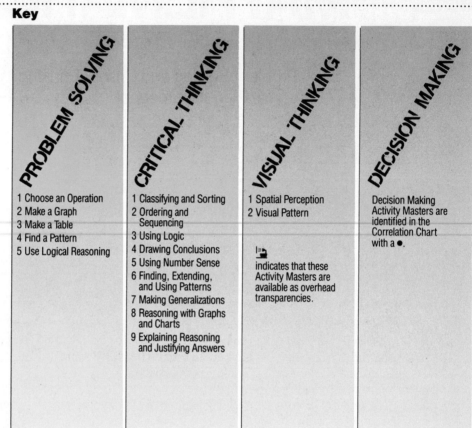

PROBLEM SOLVING
1 Choose an Operation
2 Make a Graph
3 Make a Table
4 Find a Pattern
5 Use Logical Reasoning

CRITICAL THINKING
1 Classifying and Sorting
2 Ordering and Sequencing
3 Using Logic
4 Drawing Conclusions
5 Using Number Sense
6 Finding, Extending, and Using Patterns
7 Making Generalizations
8 Reasoning with Graphs and Charts
9 Explaining Reasoning and Justifying Answers

VISUAL THINKING
1 Spatial Perception
2 Visual Pattern

indicates that these Activity Masters are available as overhead transparencies.

DECISION MAKING
Decision Making Activity Masters are identified in the Correlation Chart with a ●.

Activity/ Objective Number	Use with Pages	PROBLEM SOLVING	CRITICAL THINKING	VISUAL THINKING	DECISION MAKING
1	9-10				●
2	11-12		1		
3	13-14			1 💾	
4	15-16		1		
5	17-18			1 💾	
6	19			1 💾	
7	27-28			2	
8	29-30			2 💾	
9	31-32				●
10	35-36		5		
11	37-38				●
12	39-40	5			
13	41-42		4		
14	43-44			2 💾	
15	45		7		
16	53-54		1		
17	55-56	4			
18	57-58				●
19	59-60			1 💾	
20	61-62		4		
21	63-64	5			
22	65-66		2		
23	67-68			1 💾	
24	69-70			1 💾	
25	73-74		2		
26	75		3		
27	85-86				●
28	87-88		1		
29	89-90				●
30	91-92	2			
31	93-94		1		
32	95-96			1 💾	
33	97-98			1 💾	
34	99-100			2	
35	101-102	3			
36	103			1 💾	
37	111-112		1		
38	113-114		9		
39	115-116	3			
40	117-118			2 💾	
41	119-120		7		
42	121-122			1 💾	
43	123-124				●
44	125-126		1		
45	127-128	4			
46	129-130			2 💾	
47	131-132				●
48	133		5		
49	141-142		4		
50	143-144			1 💾	
51	145-146			2 💾	
52	147-148				●
53	149-150		6		
54	151-152		1		
55	153-154			2 💾	
56	155-156			1 💾	
57	157-158	2			
58	159-160			1 💾	
59	161				●
60	169-170			1 💾	
61	171-172	4			
62	173-174			1 💾	
63	175-176				●
64	177-178			1 💾	
65	179-180		8		
66	181-182		7		
67	183-184				●
68	185		1		
69	195-196				●
70	197-198		3		
71	199-200			2 💾	
72	201-202			1 💾	
73	203-204	2			
74	205				●
75	213-214			1 💾	
76	215-216			1 💾	
77	217-218		5		
78	219-220		1		
79	221-222	3			
80	223				●
81	231-232			2 💾	
82	233-234	2			
83	235-236			1 💾	
84	237-238		1		
85	239-240				●
86	241-242			2 💾	
87	243-244		1		
88	245-246	3			
89	247-248	5			
90	249-250		1		
91	251			1 💾	

Problem Solving and Critical Thinking Sourcebook

Purpose

Good problem solvers bring a wide variety of problem-solving strategies to bear upon a problem. After finding a solution or potential solution, they are able to look back and think critically about the solution. Successful problem solvers are resourceful and persistent in their search for a solution. The activities in this Sourcebook are designed to provide practice in problem solving and critical thinking. Students will be exposed to a wide range of problem-solving techniques. They will be given many opportunities to evaluate and criticize their solutions and decisions.

> **Successful problem solvers are resourceful and persistent in their search for a solution.**

Many of these activities will help students recognize and understand the many mathematical and real-world problem-solving situations for which there may be more than one right answer. By focusing on the problem-solving process instead of "getting the right answer," the activities encourage alternate approaches to problem situations. As such, students will find these activities to be challenging, motivating, and interesting.

How to Use This Sourcebook

You may assign pages of the Sourcebook to individual students, small groups, or the entire class. At your discretion, students may complete a page with little or no class discussion or teacher interaction. At other times you may want to teach the pages by leading a class discussion.

You may wish to introduce the activities to the class and then let students work individually or in small-group brainstorming units, which will yield a wider variety of possible approaches than students could possibly experience on their own. In some instances, you may want to use one or more activities as "Problem(s) of the Week" and give students several days to work on them individually before discussing them as a class.

Optional Overhead Transparencies are available for thirty of the Visual-Thinking activities. They can be used in a variety of ways:

- For presenting problems to the class
- For leading class discussions
- For considering possible solutions

On the reverse side of each Activity Master is a Teacher-Notes page. A sample Teacher-Notes page is shown below, along with an explanation of its main features.

Teacher Notes

Use with
Objective 78
pages 241–242

❶ Focus
Visual Thinking
Visual Patterns

Overview
This activity will provide children with an opportunity to make judgments. Children will use visual-thinking skills to find the number that doesn't belong in each row.

Materials
• tens and ones counters for each pair of children

Teaching Suggestions
Assign children to work in pairs. Distribute 9 tens and 9 ones counters to each pair. Write a two-digit number on the chalkboard, such as 87, 68, 92, 45, 73. Have children count out these numbers using tens and ones counters. Check children's work.
Direct children's attention to Master 78. Call on a volunteer to read the directions aloud. Remind children that they are looking for tens and ones. Do the first example together.
❷ Question: *Why is 87 crossed out?* [because it does not have an 8 in the ones place] Have children complete the page independently.

❸ Extension
Play "I'm Thinking of a Number" for numbers 10 through 99 with the children. Begin the game by

saying, "I'm thinking of a number that has 7 tens and 3 ones." Ask a child to write the numeral for the number. If the child is correct, he or she gives the next clue. Continue the game in this manner.

Name

VISUAL THINKING

Find the that doesn't belong in each row. Put an X on it.

48	68	87	38	98
32	62	72	27	52
51	15	54	55	56
28	29	32	22	26

Write the missing numbers.

| 16 | 26 | 36 | 46 | 56 |

Notes for Home Children find the number that does not belong in each row. Then they fill in missing numbers.

Problem Solving and Critical Thinking **EXPLORING MATHEMATICS** · Scott, Foresman and Company/1   **T78**

❶ Focus
Identifies the category of thinking skills that the activity focuses on (Problem Solving, Critical Thinking, Visual Thinking, or Decision Making) as well as the subskills that are taught.

❷ Question
Reveals and clarifies the substance of the activity, using leading or guiding questions. Students think through problems and are directed to a method of solution.

❸ Extension
Provides opportunities for students to solve new problems that stem from the original problems.

A description of each of the four categories, Problem Solving, Critical Thinking, Visual Thinking, and Decision Making, thinking skills is provided on the following pages.

Problem Solving

These activities focus students' attention on solving nonroutine problems. The activities include real-world situations to stimulate interest, while highlighting nonroutine problem-solving strategies. Students will practice and extend the skills introduced in the student text, and they will apply the general method for mathematical problem solving that is developed in the text. Many of the problems can be solved using more than one strategy, thus encouraging students to develop creative methods of their own. Students will use the following nonroutine strategies:

Make a Graph

Making a graph, or in some way graphically depicting quantitative information, will help students read values between and beyond known points, as well as organize data into more useful forms.

Make a Table

By making a table, students can organize large amounts of data and can often recognize hidden patterns that lead to general conjectures.

Find a Pattern

Identifying numerical and geometric patterns is often used in conjunction with making a table. Finding patterns allows students to find elegant solutions to otherwise difficult or tedious problems.

Use Logical Reasoning

Students use logic or deductive reasoning to determine reasonable processes and answers. This helps them solve a variety of problems.

In addition, the following routine strategy is used, largely at the beginning of the book, until students have been introduced to a variety of nonroutine strategies in the Student Edition.

Choose an Operation

Students decide which is the correct or best operation to use for a given problem. They may use this method with simple word problems as well as with multiple-step problems.

Critical Thinking

Critical Thinking activities challenge students to examine their own thinking about math and about related content areas. The problems and situations in these activities involve higher-order thinking skills such as analysis, synthesis, and evaluation. In becoming more aware and more critical of their thinking, students become better problem solvers; they learn to examine and evaluate their own reasoning. Students will use the following strategies:

Classifying and Sorting

When classifying and sorting, students identify similarities and differences among objects and elements. Students also begin to group informational components according to specific characteristics.

Ordering and Sequencing

Students learn to recognize numerical and logical order and sequence.

Using Logic

Students identify logical fallacies, hidden assumptions, and illogical structures.

Drawing Conclusions

When drawing conclusions, students use deductive and inductive reasoning. They infer and draw logical, well-founded conclusions.

Using Number Sense

Students learn to judge relevance and completeness. They determine when there is too much or too little information, and they try to make well-founded estimates.

Finding, Extending, and Using Patterns

While working on these problems, students interpolate and extrapolate number patterns and sequences. They may also infer mathematical properties.

Making Generalizations

Students build or propose a structure or they propose hypotheses. Students fit parts of a problem together to form a whole.

Reasoning with Graphs and Charts

Students learn to interpret numerical and graphical data. They interpolate and extrapolate needed information from graphs and charts.

Explaining Reasoning/ Justifying Answers

Students begin to explain their reasoning process and to justify and defend their answers.

Visual Thinking

These activities exercise students' ability to perceive and mentally manipulate visual images. They also allow some students, who may not be proficient in other areas of mathematics, to excel. Additionally, students' capacity to visualize can be extremely useful to them in solving a variety of problems and in learning to think critically. Thirty of these activities are available as overhead transparencies (optional) that can be used to facilitate class discussion of the thought processes that lead to solutions. Students will use these strategies:

Spatial Perception

These activities encourage students to recognize hidden symbols or pictures and to recognize congruent or similar figures that have been slid, flipped, or turned. Students manipulate forms mentally and create mental images.

Visual Patterns

Students learn how to infer or extend visual patterns and sequences. They are also challenged by visual analogies.

Decision Making

These activities present real-world situations that require students to make a decision. In most cases, there are no clearly right or clearly wrong answers. This gives students the opportunity to carefully weigh alternate courses of action—as well as to consider their personal experiences and preferences.

DECISION MAKING

Notes for Home   Children learn the rules and regulations when responding to a stop sign. They color the stop signs red and color the street corners that are safe.

Problem Solving and Critical Thinking/**EXPLORING MATHEMATICS** © Scott, Foresman and Company/**K**   Use after pages 9–10.

Teacher Notes

Use with
Objective 1
pages 9–10

Focus
Decision Making

Overview
The activity will provide children with an opportunity to analyze information and make decisions. Children will be asked to choose the correct response to a specific situation.

Teaching Suggestions
Draw an octagon ⬡ on the chalkboard. Explain that this is the shape of a familiar sign.
Question: *What is the name of this sign?* [a stop sign] Write the word STOP inside the shape. Explain that the shape of this sign means the same thing as the word stop. Discuss what drivers and pedestrians should do when they see stop signs.

Have children think of other signs they have seen on the way to school. Draw them on the board. Talk about what each one means.

Distribute copies of Master 1 to the children. Direct children's attention to the shape in the center of the page. **Questions:** *What kind of sign is this?* [a stop sign] *What color is a stop sign?* [red] *Can you find other stop signs on the page?* [yes] Color all the stop signs red.

Discuss with children what a stop sign tells people to do. Call on volunteers to explain their answers. Then have them color the corners of the street that show children following the rules of a stop sign.

Extension
Challenge children to make up their own signs for a rule in the classroom. Have them draw the sign and explain the rule to the class. Post the signs around the classroom for the children to follow.

Name _____

DECISION MAKING

STOP

MAIL

Notes for Home Children learn the rules and regulations when responding to a stop sign. They color the stop signs red and color the street corners that are safe.

CRITICAL THINKING

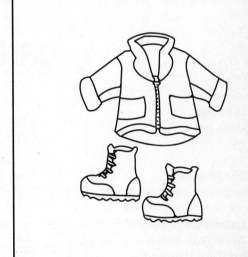

Notes for Home Children use visual clues to decide how objects should be grouped. Then they draw a line to each bear's outfit.

Teacher Notes

Use with
Objective 2
  pages 11–12

Focus
Critical Thinking
  Classifying and Sorting

Overview
Critical-thinking activities will provide children with opportunities to classify objects by using logical reasoning. Children will use visual clues to classify and sort objects that are intended for certain items.

Materials
- 1 large doll
- 1 small doll
- 1 large paper hat
- 1 small paper hat

Teaching Suggestions
Display a large doll and a small doll to the class. Then show the large and small paper hats. Select a volunteer to match the hats with the dolls. Explain that by looking at the two hats and the two dolls, the small hat will not fit the large doll. Have the volunteer put the hats on the dolls to show the correct fit.

Direct children's attention to Master 2. Tell the children that this is a bear family that needs to get dressed for a walk. Ask them to study the three jackets and shoes. Have children tell about the clues that will help them match the correct outfits to each bear. When they are sure of their choices, children should match the outfit to the right bear by drawing a line to each item.

Have the children complete the page independently. Let them color the outfits after matching the items. Call on children to show their picture and explain how they matched the outfit to each bear.

Extension
Have children work in groups of three or four. Ask one child to line up three chairs of different sizes. Then have the other group members sit in a chair that would fit them the best. Have them explain their choice.

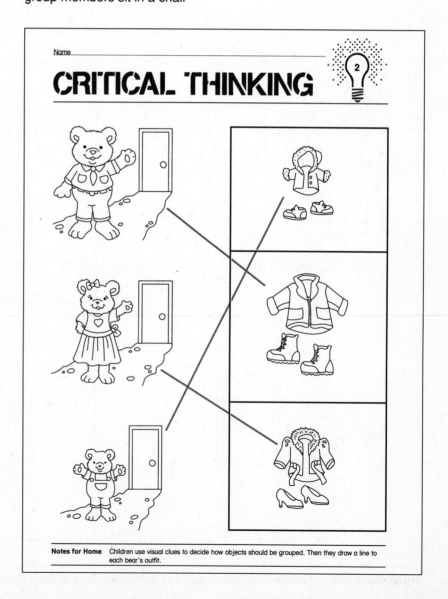

VISUAL THINKING

3

Notes for Home Children ring the object that does not belong in each group.

Use with

Objective 3
   pages 13–14

Focus

Visual Thinking
   Spatial Perception

Overview

Classifying activities will provide children with an opportunity to think analytically and logically. Children will learn to notice the similarities and differences among objects.

Materials

• newspaper, book, magazine
• crayon
• box of small objects (for each group)

Teaching Suggestions

Display a newspaper, a book, a magazine, and a crayon on a table. Ask the children to identify the objects. Have them describe how the objects are alike and how they are different. Then ask them to name the object that doesn't belong. Repeat with other groups of objects, having children first determine the common characteristic of the objects.

Assign children to work in groups of four. Distribute a box of items to each group. Ask each group to find ways they can sort the objects. Explain that objects can be sorted by color, size, or use. Ask each group to explain what they have done with the objects.

Direct children's attention to Master 3. Have them identify the objects. Tell children to study the objects in each box. Then determine the property in which they have in common. Ask them to ring the object that does not belong in each group. Call on volunteers to explain their answers.

Extension

Distribute magazines, drawing paper, paste, and scissors to the class. Ask children to cut out two objects from a magazine that have similar characteristics. Have them paste their pictures on a sheet of paper. Call on various children to show their pictures. Have them explain why they chose the objects and how they are alike.

Name _____

VISUAL THINKING

Notes for Home   Children ring the object that does not belong in each group.

CRITICAL THINKING

Notes for Home Children learn to find objects in the correct locations. They mark the objects with an X that do not belong in the picture.

Teacher Notes

Use with
Objective 4
    pages 15–16

Focus
Critical Thinking
    Classifying and Sorting

Overview
Critical thinking activities will provide children with opportunities to think analytically and logically. Children will sort objects according to their proper locations.

Teaching Suggestions
Draw a large tree on the chalkboard, showing its roots and branches. **Questions:** *What part of this tree is above ground? What part is below ground? Where should I draw a line to show where the ground would be?* Ask children to suggest plants, animals, rocks, and other objects that can be found below the ground; above the tree branches; and above the ground but between the tree roots and branches.

Distribute copies of Master 4. Direct children's attention to the wavy lines across the middle of the page. Explain that this line shows the top of the ocean. Point out that the water skier is on the water. Ask children to look at the objects above the water line. Have them cross out objects that don't belong above the water. Then have children look at objects below the water line. Have them cross out objects that don't belong below the water line.

Extension
Play the game of "I Spy" with the children using directional words such as *above, top, below,* and *between.* Explain that you will think of an object in the classroom. Give clues so that they can guess the object. Choose a clearly visible object. Give a clue using the lesson vocabulary, such as "I spy something below the clock." Give additional clues as needed, such as "It is between the top and the bottom of the bulletin board."

After children have correctly guessed several objects, have a child select an object and whisper his or her clue to you. Help the child say the clues aloud and call on other children to guess the name of the object.

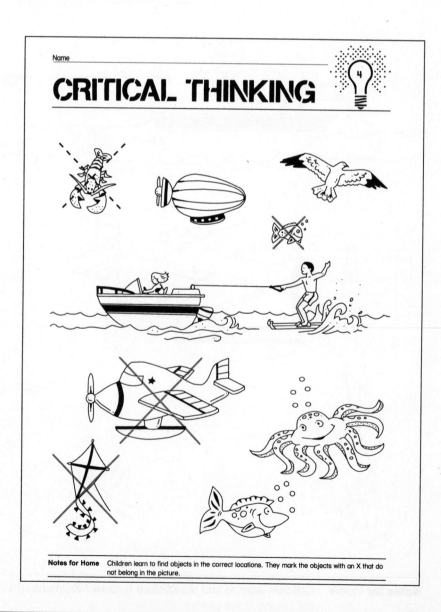

Name _____

CRITICAL THINKING

Notes for Home Children learn to find objects in the correct locations. They mark the objects with an X that do not belong in the picture.

VISUAL THINKING

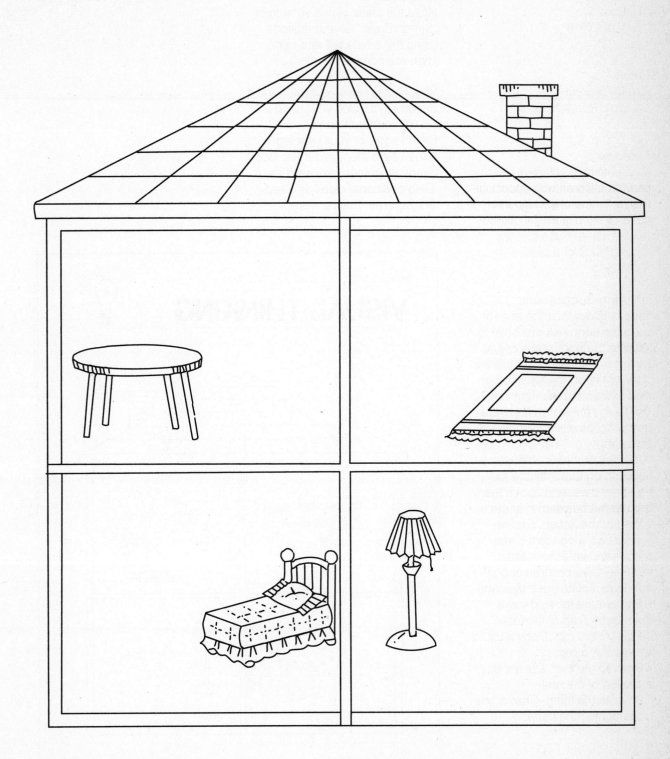

Notes for Home Children learn to use visual clues to draw missing objects.

Problem Solving and Critical Thinking/**EXPLORING MATHEMATICS** © Scott, Foresman and Company/K   Use after pages 17–18.

Teacher Notes

Use with
Objective 5
   pages 17–18

Focus
Visual Thinking
   Spatial Perception

Overview
Visual-thinking activities will provide children with experience in analyzing and observing information from pictures. Children will use visual clues to draw missing parts of a picture.

Teaching Suggestions
Have children face the front of the classroom. Ask one child to come to the front and stand at the left side (still facing the front of the classroom). Ask another child to stand at the right side (still facing the front). Have children practice distinguishing left from right.

   Distribute copies of Master 5. Tell children that they are looking at the inside of a doll house. Discuss what is shown in each "room" of the house. Explain that you will give them some directions. Have them listen carefully. Give children enough time to complete each direction.

   Point to the table. Draw a chair to the right of the table.

   Point to the rug. Draw a cat to the left of the rug.

   Point to the bed. Draw a ball to the left of the bed.

   Point to the lamp. Draw a box to the right of the lamp.

Extension
Have the class play a version of "Simon Says." Give directions using the words *left* and *right.* Here are some examples:

Simon says raise your left hand.
Simon says touch your head
   with your right hand.
Simon says lift your right leg.
Simon says stomp your left foot.
Simon says touch your left ear.

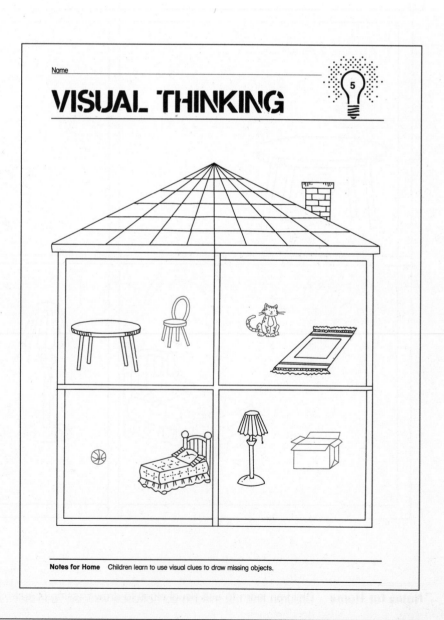

Name _____

VISUAL THINKING

Notes for Home   Children learn to use visual clues to draw missing objects.

VISUAL THINKING

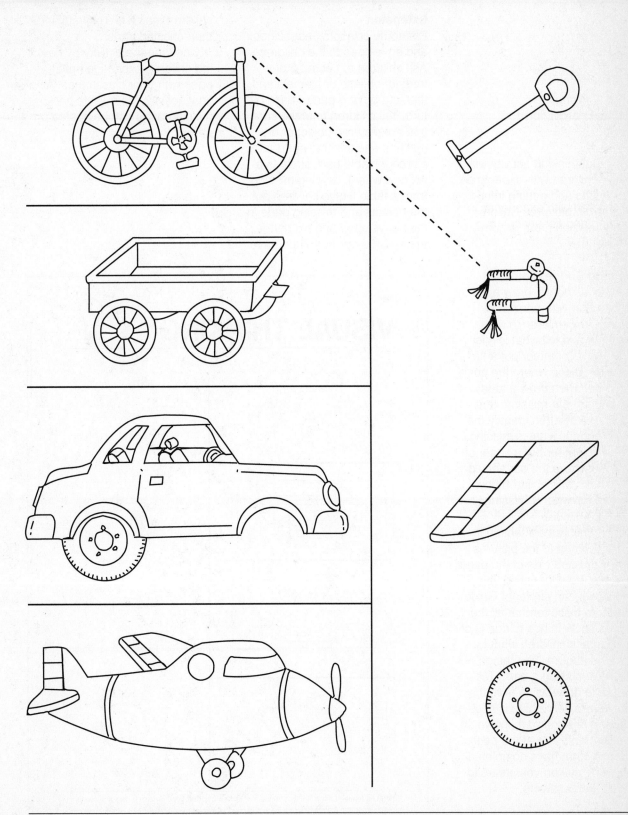

Notes for Home   Children find the missing part of each vehicle. Then they draw a line to show where each part belongs.

Use with
Objective 6
    page 19

Focus
Visual Thinking
    Spatial Perception

Overview
This visual-thinking activity will provide children with experience in analyzing and getting information from pictures. Children identify missing parts to complete pictures.

Teaching Suggestions
On the chalkboard, draw a picture of a star with one point missing. Ask children to name the object and tell what is missing. Have a volunteer put a finger on the place where the point should be. Then draw a teddy bear with an ear missing, and again have children identify the picture and tell what is missing. Have a volunteer put a finger on the place where the ear should be. Discuss with children how they can tell what is missing from each picture.

Direct children's attention to Master 6. Point to the pictures on the left-hand side of the page and have them identified. [bicycle, wagon, car, airplane] Guide children to discover that all the pictures show things to ride in or on. Then ask children what is the same about all the things. [They are missing a part.] Tell children to draw a line from the place where something is missing to the missing part shown on the right-hand side of the page. When children have completed their work, call on volunteers to explain their answers.

Extension
Distribute scissors, magazines, and envelopes to the children. Ask children to cut out 5 pictures of objects or animals and then cut off one part of each picture. Tell children to make sure that the pictured object or animal has one missing part that is a recognizable part, such as a tail or a wheel, or a leg missing from a table. Have children put the objects and missing parts in their envelopes and exchange them with a partner. Then have children match the objects and their missing parts.

Continue the activity by having children exchange envelopes with their classmates. As a final activity, the objects and missing parts can be pasted on paper.

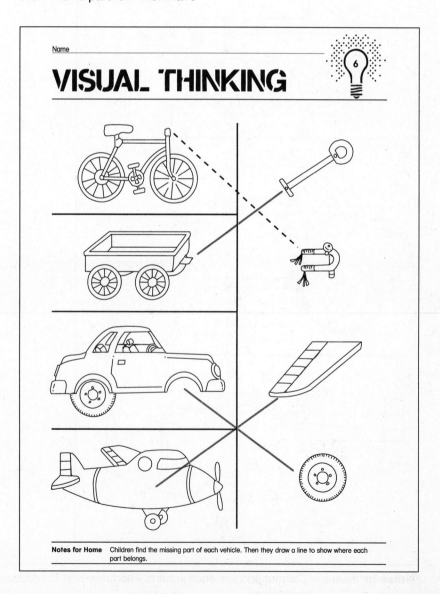

Name _____

VISUAL THINKING

Notes for Home Children find the missing part of each vehicle. Then they draw a line to show where each part belongs.

VISUAL THINKING

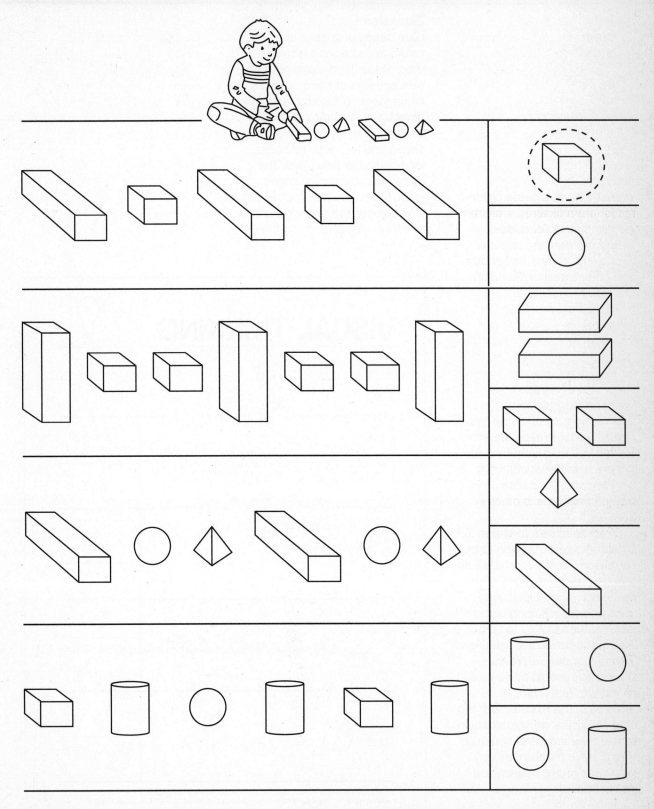

Notes for Home   Children identify each pattern. Then they ring the picture that continues the pattern.

Use with
Objective 7
  pages 27–28

Focus
Visual Thinking
  Visual Patterns

Overview
This activity will provide children with an opportunity to analyze and complete a sequence. Children identify the patterns and ring the picture that shows what comes next in the pattern.

Materials
• crayons
• pencils

Teaching Suggestions
Display this pattern on the table: crayon, pencil, crayon, pencil. Have the objects identified. Ask children to tell what object comes next in the pattern. [crayon] Repeat with other objects.

Distribute copies of Master 7. Direct children's attention to the patterns in the first row. Have a volunteer describe the pattern. [long block, short block, long block, short block, long block] Have children look at the pictures in the box at the right. Ask them to ring the picture that shows what should come next in the pattern. [short block] Continue in this manner with the other rows. Call on volunteers to explain their answers. You may want to have children tell why the other pictures in each row are not correct.

Extension
Give beads and laces of several colors and shapes to the children. Have them make up their own patterns of beads and string them on the lace to make a necklace. You may wish to have children begin with one shape and two or three colors, increasing the difficulty of the pattern as their ability allows.

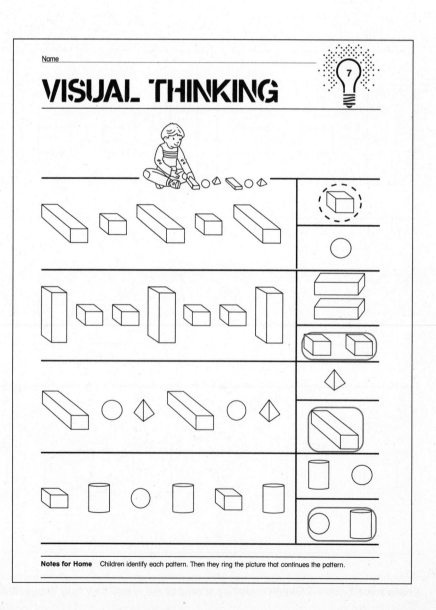

Name _____

VISUAL THINKING

Notes for Home   Children identify each pattern. Then they ring the picture that continues the pattern.

VISUAL THINKING

Notes for Home   Children identify patterns of animals. Then they draw a line from each animal to their parade.

Use with
Objective 8
pages 29–30

Focus
Visual Thinking
Visual Patterns

Overview
Visual thinking activities will provide children with experience in identifying and copying a pattern. Children will identify and copy patterns that involve animal figures.

Teaching Suggestions
Help children arrange themselves in patterns, such as girl-boy-girl-boy or two girls-one boy-two girls-one boy. Ask children to suggest additional patterns by using different objects, such as beads.

Distribute copies of Master 8. Discuss the page with the class. Explain that three parades need animals to join them. Tell children to look for a pattern in each parade. Have them decide where each animal belongs. Then they can draw a line from each animal to the correct parade. Call on volunteers to explain their answers.

Extension
Distribute magazines, drawing paper, paste, and scissors to the children. Ask children to cut out pictures that will form this pattern: Object 1-Object 2-Object 1-Object 2. Explain that they will need two different types of objects, such as houses, cars, dogs, or people. Point out that

they must find at least two of each object to make this pattern. Tell children that they may continue the pattern with as many pictures as they can find.

Name _____

VISUAL THINKING

Notes for Home Children identify patterns of animals. Then they draw a line from each animal to their parade.

DECISION MAKING

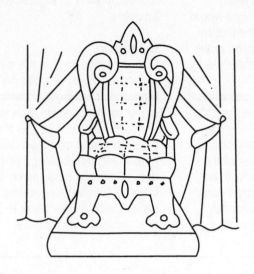

Notes for Home   Children use picture clues to match fairy tale characters with storybook settings.

Teacher Notes

Use with
Objective 9
    pages 31–32

Focus
Decision Making

Overview
This activity will provide children with an opportunity to draw conclusions. Children will look for picture details before matching pictures.

Teaching Suggestions
Place 3 books on a table. Call on four children to stand near that table. **Questions:** *Are there enough books to give each child 1 book?* [no] *How can you tell?* [by giving each child a book; by counting the number of books and the number of children]

Ask 1 child to sit down. **Question:** *Are there enough books to give each child 1 book?* [yes] Repeat the activity with 4 books and five children; 2 books and three children.

Direct children's attention to Master 9. Ask children to identify the pictures on the left side of the page. [a throne, rocking chairs by a fireplace, 3 houses made of different material—straw, sticks, bricks] Then point out the pictures on the right side. Have children identify the pictures. [3 pigs, a king, 3 bears, a dog]

Do the first row with the children. Have them count the thrones in the top picture. **Questions:** *How many people can sit on one throne?* [1] *What kind of person usually sits on a*

throne? [a king or a queen] *Which picture on the right would go with the throne?* [the picture of the king] Have children draw the line to match the throne and the king.

Remind children to use clues in the pictures to make their decisions about matching the other places and animal characters. Explain that one of the pictures at the right will not be used. Then have children complete the page independently. When the work is completed, ask volunteers to explain their answers.

Extension
Remind children that the picture of the dog was not used on Master 9. Distribute drawing paper to the children. Ask them to draw their own dog on the drawing paper and then draw something that belongs with a dog. (Possible responses: 1 bone; 1 leash; 1 doghouse; 1 bowl) Call on volunteers to show and explain their pictures.

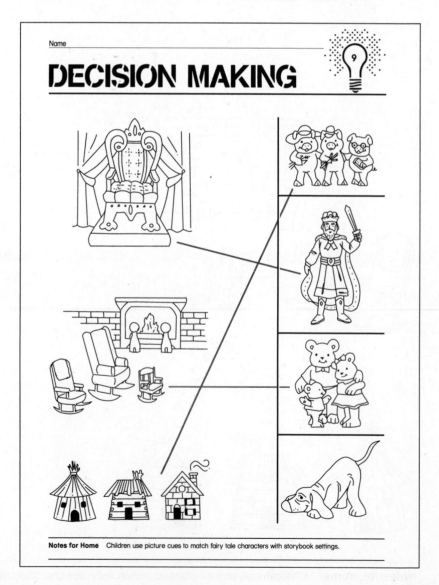

Name

DECISION MAKING

Notes for Home   Children use picture cues to match fairy tale characters with storybook settings.

CRITICAL THINKING

Notes for Home   Children compare objects to make equal groups. They draw missing objects if there are too few and mark an X on objects that are too many.

Problem Solving and Critical Thinking/**EXPLORING MATHEMATICS** © Scott, Foresman and Company/K   Use after pages 35–36.

Teacher Notes

Use with
Objective 10
   pages 35–36

Focus
Critical Thinking
   Using Number Sense

Overview
The activity will provide children with the opportunity to think analytically and logically. Children will compare groups to determine what is needed to make them equal in number.

Materials
• crayons
• 10 counters

Teaching Suggestions
Have children work in groups of four. Give each group 4 crayons. Then give each group ten counters. Ask children to use some counters to form a larger group than the crayons. Check children's work. Then have them form a group of counters that has fewer objects than the crayons.

   Distribute copies of Master 10. Direct children's attention to the page. Explain that the picture on the wall shows a clown doing his circus act. The three clowns at the right are getting dressed for their performance. The shelves hold their clothing and equipment.

   Ask children to compare the three clowns with the clown in the picture. Have them identify what each clown still needs. Tell them to look at the top shelf with the hats. **Question:** *Are there enough hats for each clown to have on?* [No. There are fewer hats than clowns.] Have children draw another hat on the shelf.

Then tell children to decide if there are enough collars, balls, and horns for the clowns. Have them put an X on the extra object and draw an object if there are too few. Allow children time to complete the worksheet independently and to color the Master. Have volunteers explain their answers.

Extension
Provide children with a sheet of paper that has been divided into three sections. Draw six circles on the chalkboard and ask children to draw and color in the same amount of circles (or any other simple shape) in the first section of their paper. Have children use a red crayon. In the second section, have children draw more green circles than red circles. In the third section, have children draw less blue circles than red circles. Check the children's activity.

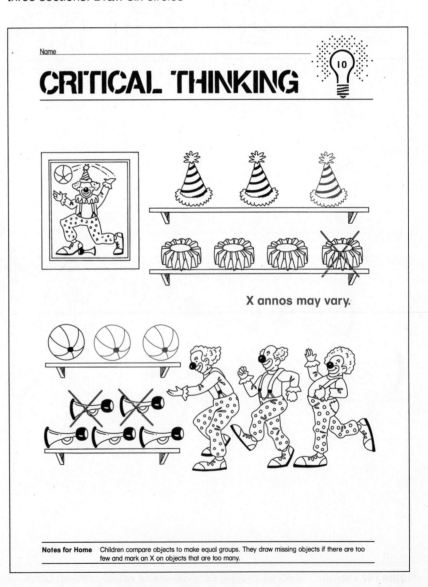

Name _____

CRITICAL THINKING   10

X annos may vary.

Notes for Home   Children compare objects to make equal groups. They draw missing objects if there are too few and mark an X on objects that are too many.

DECISION MAKING

Notes for Home   Children make a decision about where children can sit on a Ferris wheel.

Teacher Notes

Use with
Objective 11
    pages 37–38

Focus
Decision Making

Overview
This activity will provide children with an opportunity to draw conclusions. Children will determine where a boy and a girl will sit on a Ferris wheel.

Teaching Suggestions
Talk with children about the number of items they need to wear in order to get dressed. **Questions:** *What do you need to get dressed? How many shirts do you need? How many socks (shoes, hats, mittens, boots, coats) do you need?*

List children's answers on the chalkboard. Read the list with the children and help them group their answers into categories: 2 and 1.

Direct children's attention to Master 11. Ask children to tell what they see. [children on a Ferris wheel] Invite children to briefly share any personal experiences of riding on a Ferris wheel. Then explain that each seat on a Ferris wheel holds two people. Ask children to look at the cars. **Questions:** *Are all the cars full?* [no] *Are any cars empty?* [no] *Can 2 more children get on?* [yes] Tell children to draw a line from the boy and from the girl to show where they might sit on the Ferris wheel. Have children discuss their answers.

Extension
Play a game of "Simon Says" with the children. Have them listen to and follow instructions involving one or two things, such as the following:

Raise 2 arms.
Cover 1 ear.
Show 2 fingers.
Hop on 1 foot.
Clap 2 times.

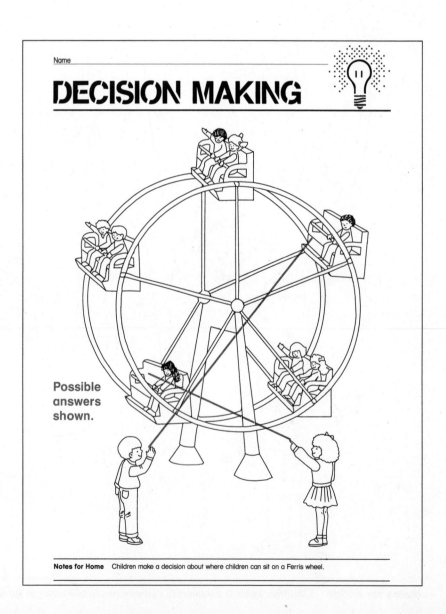

Name _____

DECISION MAKING

Possible answers shown.

Notes for Home   Children make a decision about where children can sit on a Ferris wheel.

PROBLEM SOLVING

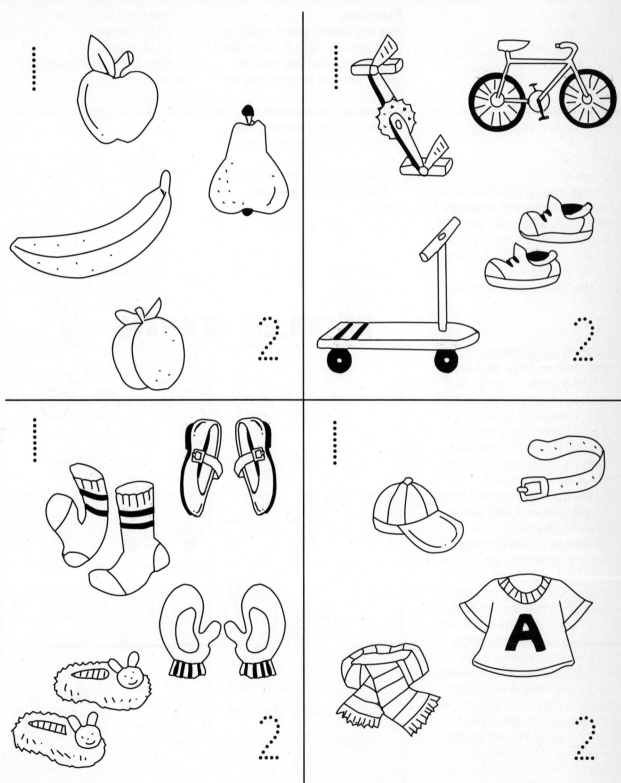

Notes for Home Children identify how many objects are in each group by writing the number.

Use after pages 39–40.

Teacher Notes

Use with
Objective 12
   pages 39–40

Focus
Problem Solving
   Use Logical Reasoning

Overview
Problem-solving activities will provide children with opportunities to think analytically and logically. Children will identify the common characteristics of some objects and then select the numeral that belongs with the group.

Teaching Suggestions
Have children close their eyes and listen for the sounds you will make. Clap your hands two times. **Question:** *How many times did I clap?* [2 times] Then clap your hands one time and ask the question again. Repeat the activity with different sounds, such as bells or a buzzer, limiting them to one or two sounds each time.

   Distribute copies of Master 12. Direct children's attention to the page. Have children identify the pictures. Explain that they are to study the pictures in each group. Have them decide which of the two numerals belongs with the objects in the group. Have children trace the numeral that belongs with the pictures, and then color each object. Call on volunteers to identify what is in each box and to explain the reasons for their choices.

Extension
Play a guessing game involving the numbers 1 and 2. Have children guess what you have in mind. Here are some examples:

   There is 1 in our room.
   It is green and made of felt.
   What is it? [a flannel board]

   I see 2 of these in the room.
   They are round and can bounce.
   What are they? [balls]

   There is 1 in our room.
   It has four chairs.
   It has 4 legs.
   What is it? [math/reading table]

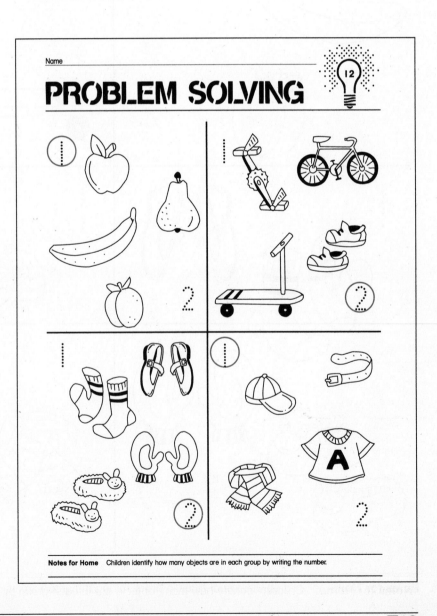

Name _____

PROBLEM SOLVING

Notes for Home   Children identify how many objects are in each group by writing the number.

CRITICAL THINKING

Notes for Home Children use visual clues in order to ring the group that is coming to visit.

Teacher Notes

Use with
Objective 13
  pages 41–42

Focus
Critical Thinking
  Drawing Conclusions

Overview
These activities will provide children with an opportunity to think analytically and logically. Children will use visual clues to determine who will be using the objects shown.

Materials
• pictures of three dogs

Teaching Suggestions
Display the three dogs on the chalkboard. Have children count the dogs. **Questions:** *If you had three dogs, how many collars would you need?* [3] *How many leashes?* [3]

Distribute copies of Master 13. Direct children's attention to the page. Explain that they are to use clues in the picture in order to decide who is coming to the house. (The picture of the house gives clues; the bottom picture gives two possible answers.) Ask children to study the picture, decide which group is coming to visit, and to ring and color the correct answer. [the triplets] Call on volunteers to explain the answer and to point out specific clues they used in the picture.

Extension
Play a game of "Follow the Threes," a cumulative game in which children will need to remember and perform actions in groups of three. Give one instruction, such as "Clap 3 times." Have a child follow your instruction. Then ask that child to repeat your instruction and add a second one, such as "Jump 3 times." Call on another child to perform both actions. Have this volunteer repeat the first two instructions and add one of his/her own that involves doing something three times. Then another child follows all three instructions, repeats them, and adds a fourth instruction. Begin a new game.

Name _____

CRITICAL THINKING   13

Notes for Home   Children use visual clues in order to ring the group that is coming to visit.

VISUAL THINKING

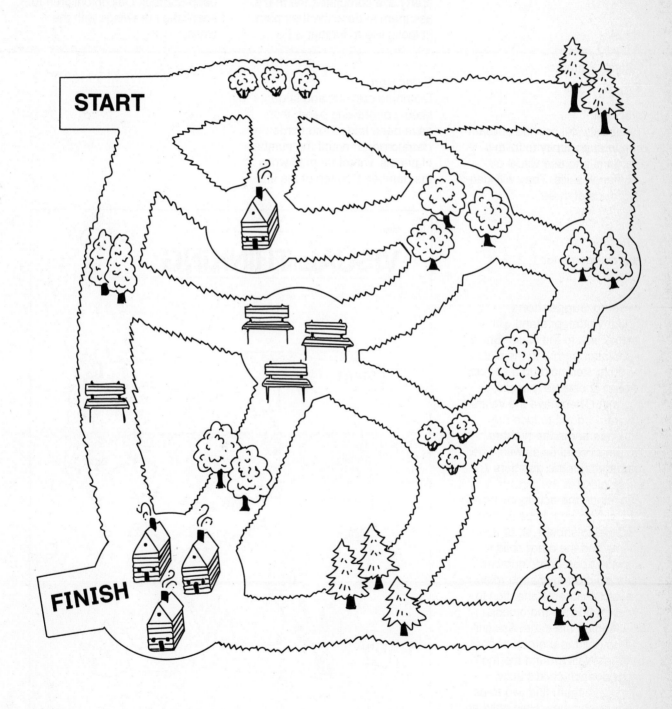

START

FINISH

Notes for Home Children identify groups of three objects. Then they follow the groups of three from start to finish.

Use with
Objective 14
    pages 43–44

Focus
Visual Thinking
    Visual Patterns

Overview
The activity will provide children with an opportunity to follow directions and use visual discrimination skills. They will identify groups of three.

Materials
• number cards for 1, 2, 3

Teaching Suggestions
Have a volunteer stand with her/his back to the class. Show the number card 3 to the class. Have children hold up a correct number of objects (pencils, crayons). Then have the volunteer turn around to face the class and name the number. Repeat several times with other volunteers for the numbers 1 and 2.

Continue the activity by having children work in pairs. Ask one child to show 1, 2, or 3 objects and the other child to write the appropriate number. Have children exchange roles.

Direct children's attention to Master 14. Have the objects identified on the page. Ask children to point to a group of one cottage. Walk around the room to check each child's activity. Then have them find two trees and three bushes. Help children identify the words START and FINISH. Explain that they will

find the path from START that leads to all the groups of three and ends at FINISH. When children have completed the maze, ask them to describe their path. [It looks like a number 3.]

Extension
Distribute crayons and large sheets of drawing paper that have been folded into thirds. Have children count the number of panels. Direct them to write the number 1 on top of the first panel, 2 on the middle panel, and 3 on the last panel. Have them draw a picture to go with each number. Call on children to share their drawings with the class.

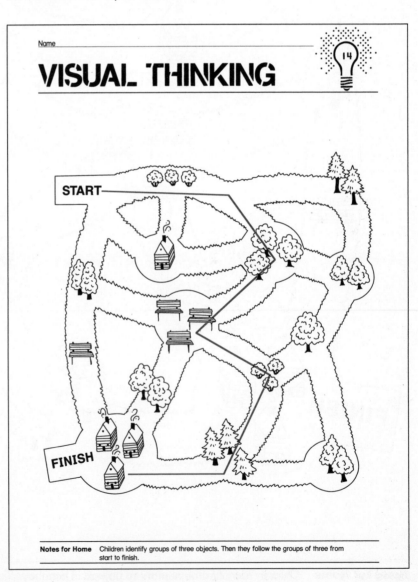

Name _____

VISUAL THINKING

START

FINISH

Notes for Home   Children identify groups of three objects. Then they follow the groups of three from start to finish.

CRITICAL THINKING

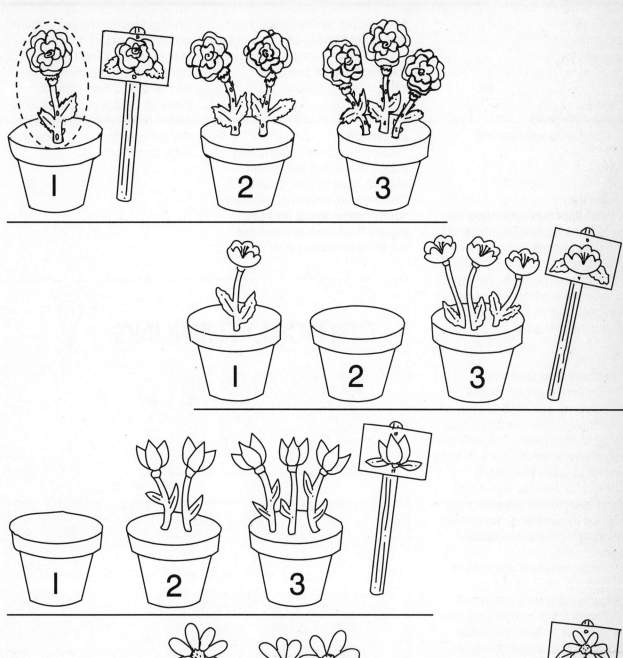

Notes for Home   Children compare the number of flowers in each row. Then they color in the number of flowers for each pot.

Use with
Objective 15
    page 45

Focus
Critical Thinking
    Making Generalizations

Overview
Children will have the opportunity to think critically by recognizing generalizations that can be drawn from examples. Children will compare pictures, identify similarities, and determine generalizations that can be made about the groups.

Teaching Suggestions
Write these numbers on the chalkboard: 1, 2, 3. Call on a volunteer to draw 1 smiling face next to the numeral 1; 2 smiling faces next to the numeral 2; and 3 smiling faces next to the numeral 3. Repeat with other symbols. Explain the similarities with each number group and the relationship between number and symbol.

Direct children's attention to Master 15. Discuss the page with the children. Explain that there are signs next to each row of flower pots. Ask children to compare the flowers in the first row of pots with the flower on the sign. **Question:** *What kind of flowers should be in all the pots next to this sign?* [rose] For practice have them draw a rose on a piece of paper. Let them color the rose that is shown with a dotted line on the Master.

Next point out that each flower pot has a number on it.

Ask children to draw the correct number of flowers and the right kind of flower in each empty pot. Have volunteers show and explain their answers.

Extension
Distribute colored construction paper, drawing paper, green crayons, scissors, and paste. Demonstrate how to draw three flower stems on the drawing paper. Then have children cut out three blossoms from construction paper and paste them onto the stems. (Each flower may be of a different type and/or color.) Encourage children to add details to their pictures. Have an exhibit of their pictures on the bulletin board. Discuss any patterns that may appear in each child's picture.

Name _____

CRITICAL THINKING

15

Notes for Home   Children compare the number of flowers in each row. Then they color in the number of flowers for each pot.

CRITICAL THINKING

Notes for Home   Children identify objects with four of the same parts by marking an X.

Problem Solving and Critical Thinking/**EXPLORING MATHEMATICS** © Scott, Foresman and Company/K   Use after pages 53–54.

Use with
Objective 16
pages 53–54

Focus
Critical Thinking
Classifying and Sorting

Overview
This critical-thinking activity will provide children with an opportunity to think analytically and logically. Children will identify objects that have a common characteristic, four of the same part.

Teaching Suggestions
On the chalkboard, draw a flower with three petals and a stem, another with four petals and a stem, and a third with three petals and four leaves on its stem. **Question:** *Who can find a shape with four of something on it?* Children should ring both the flower with four petals and the flower with four leaves on the stem. Have children count to four as you point to the petals and the leaves.

Distribute copies of Master 16 and direct children's attention to the page. Point to Mr. Four (the character with a head that looks like a numeral four) in the picture. Explain that Mr. Four is only looking for furniture that has four of the same part. Point out the two tables next to Mr. Four and have children count the legs on each. Explain the difference between the table with three legs and the table with four legs. Have them mark an X and color the table with

four legs. Direct the children to mark an X on all the objects in the picture that have four of the same part. Then have them color and complete the page independently.

Extension
Assign children to work in pairs. Give each pair of children counters, not less than thirty-two and an egg carton with the numbers 1 through 4 written in the cups.

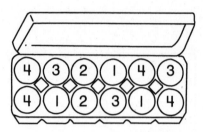

Have children fill each cup with the correct number of counters.

Name _____

CRITICAL THINKING

Notes for Home   Children identify objects with four of the same parts by marking an X.

PROBLEM SOLVING

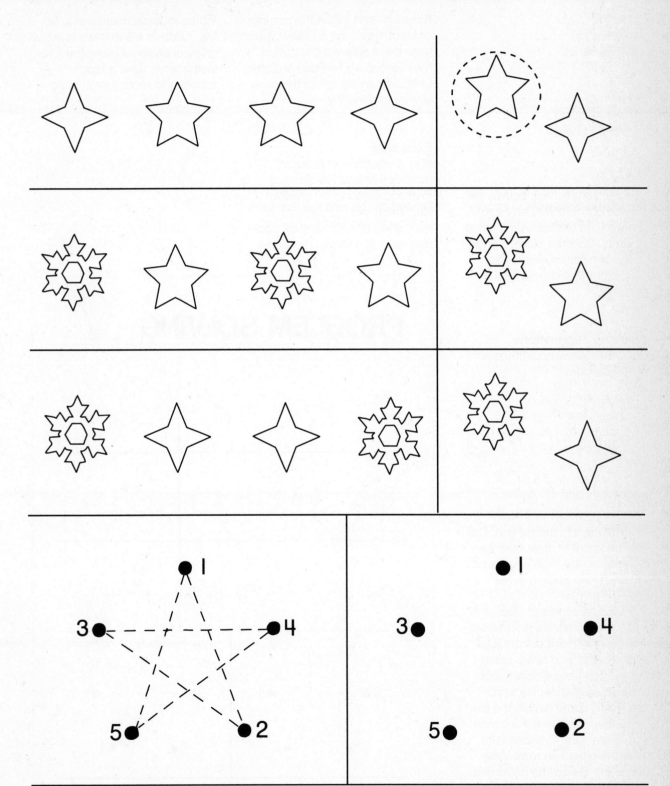

Notes for Home   Children find and ring the next object in a pattern. Then they follow a number pattern to complete a picture.

Problem Solving and Critical Thinking/**EXPLORING MATHEMATICS** © Scott, Foresman and Company/**K**   Use after pages 55–56.

Use with
Objective 17
    pages 55–56

Focus
Problem Solving
    Find a Pattern

Overview
This problem-solving activity will provide children with an opportunity to use strategies in finding patterns. Children study a given series of pictures and will find the picture that comes next in the pattern.

Teaching Suggestions
Draw the following patterns on the chalkboard.

Point to each row and have children identify the pattern. Call on volunteers to draw their own patterns on the chalkboard and to explain the pattern to the class.

   Distribute copies of Master 17 and direct children's attention to the first row. Point out the four-pointed stars and five-pointed stars. Then have children look at the stars and decide which star would come next in the pattern. Have them ring the correct star to the right. Children complete the other two rows independently. Below the patterned rows are two incomplete stars. Point out the star on the left.

Have children follow the number order of 1 through 5 orally. Then have them connect the dotted lines to make a five-pointed star. Children can complete the other star independently.

Extension
Play a selection of musical records that have interesting rhythmic patterns for children. Help them identify patterns in each song or recording by clapping out the rhythm. Then distribute musical instruments to the children. Have them practice musical patterns using the instruments. Use a tape recorder to record each song.

Name _____

DECISION MAKING

Notes for Home   Children use picture clues to get information. Then they write the missing numbers on the teammate shirts.

Problem Solving and Critical Thinking/**EXPLORING MATHEMATICS** © Scott, Foresman and Company/**K**   Use after pages 57–58.

Use with

Objective 18
    pages 57–58

Focus

Decision Making

Overview

This activity will provide children with an opportunity to analyze a problem and identify information needed for making a decision. Children will study a picture to find the answer to a given question.

Materials

• colored chalk

Teaching Suggestions

Write several sets of the numbers 4 and 5 on the chalkboard. Call on as many children to trace over the numbers using colored chalk.

Distribute copies of Master 18. Discuss the Master with the children. Point out that the picture shows a ballfield with children from three teams. Some children are practicing on the field. Point to the batters at the bottom of the Master. By studying the picture, explain to the children that they have to decide which team these new players will join. Have children write the correct number on each child's T-shirt. Call on volunteers to explain how they found their clues.

Extension

Have children work in groups of five. Give each group a large sheet of posterboard with the numbers 1-5 written down the left side. Supplies needed are magazines, scissors, and paste.

1.
2.
3.
4.
5.

Assign each group member to a number. Then have children cut out pictures and paste groups of like objects next to their assigned number. When completed, have groups display their posters. Discuss each poster with the class.

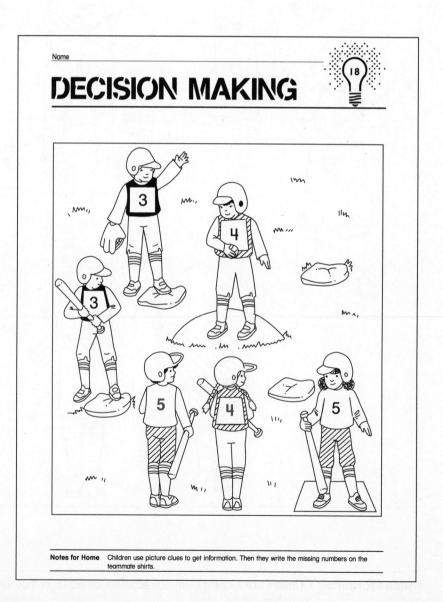

Name _____

DECISION MAKING

Notes for Home   Children use picture clues to get information. Then they write the missing numbers on the teammate shirts.

VISUAL THINKING

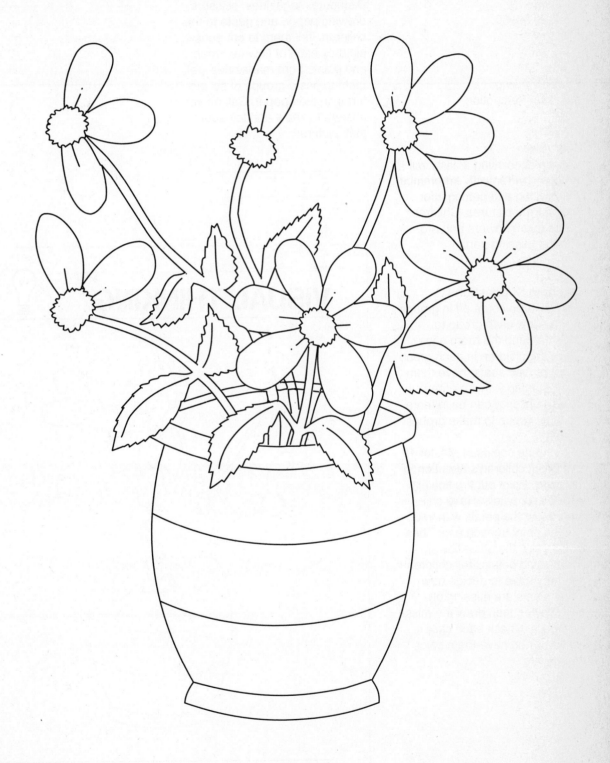

Notes for Home   Children draw petals so that each flower has 6.

Teacher Notes

Use with
Objective 19
pages 59–60

Focus
Visual Thinking
Spatial Perception

Overview
This visual-thinking activity will provide children with experience in analyzing and getting information from pictures. Children will compare flowers and provide the missing parts.

Teaching Suggestions
Help children count off in groups of six. Allow each group to march around the room once. When the children in each group return to their seats, have them count starting with 1 as they sit down. (Children can be in more than one group to make groups of six.)

Distribute copies of Master 19 and direct children's attention to the page. Point out the flower with the six petals. Have children count the petals with you as they point to each one. Then explain that the other flowers are missing petals. Tell children that they have to decide how many petals are missing on each flower, then draw the missing petals. Check each child's activity. Then have them color the flowers.

Extension
Distribute magazines, scissors, drawing paper, and paste to the children. Tell them to cut out six pictures each of flowers, trees, and plants from magazines. Tell them to paste groups of six pictures on their paper. Call on volunteers to show and tell about their pictures.

Name _____

VISUAL THINKING

Notes for Home   Children draw petals so that each flower has 6.

CRITICAL THINKING

20

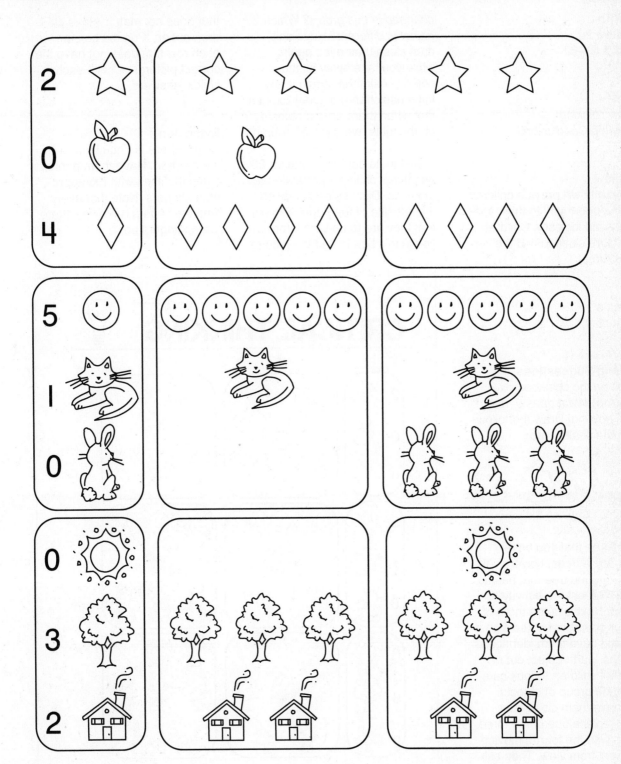

Notes for Home   Children put an X on the picture that does not match the box on the left.

Teacher Notes

Use with
Objective 20
   pages 61–62

Focus
Critical Thinking
   Drawing Conclusions

Overview
This activity will provide children with an opportunity to think analytically and logically. Children use picture clues to find the correct pictures.

Materials
• 4 objects

Teaching Suggestions
Write 0 on the chalkboard. **Question:** *What does 0 mean?* [none, nothing] Draw the following on the chalkboard:

Tell children that you have drawn apple trees. Have a volunteer ring the tree that has no apples. Repeat the activity as needed. Next arrange three of the four classroom objects on a table and have them identified. Keep the fourth object out of sight. Tell children to look carefully at the group of objects. Then have them close their eyes. Replace one of the three objects with the fourth, moving the object from view. Then ask children to look at the group once more. **Questions:** *Are the objects the same? Has anything changed in this group? Which object is different?* Have children close their eyes again while you take away all the objects. Ask them again if anything has changed. [yes] Explain that when there are no objects on the table, we call it a group of zero.

Distribute copies of Master 20 and direct children's attention to the rows. Discuss each box on the left side of the page. Explain that they are to use the information in this box to find the picture that does not match. Have children put an X on the box in each row that does <u>not</u> have the correct pictures. Check each child's answers.

Extension
Sing "Where is Thumbkin" with the children. Have them pantomime the lines with the appropriate fingers. Note that every time the fingers run away, there are <u>no</u> fingers up.

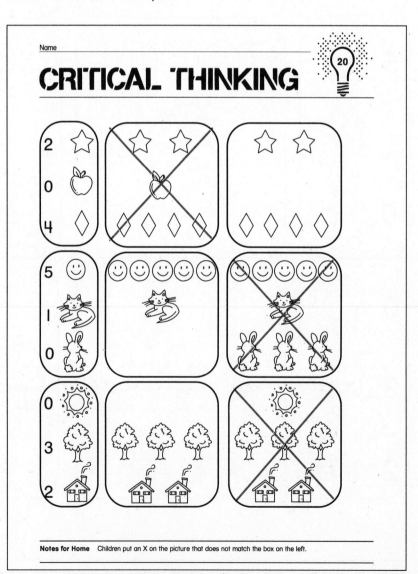

PROBLEM SOLVING

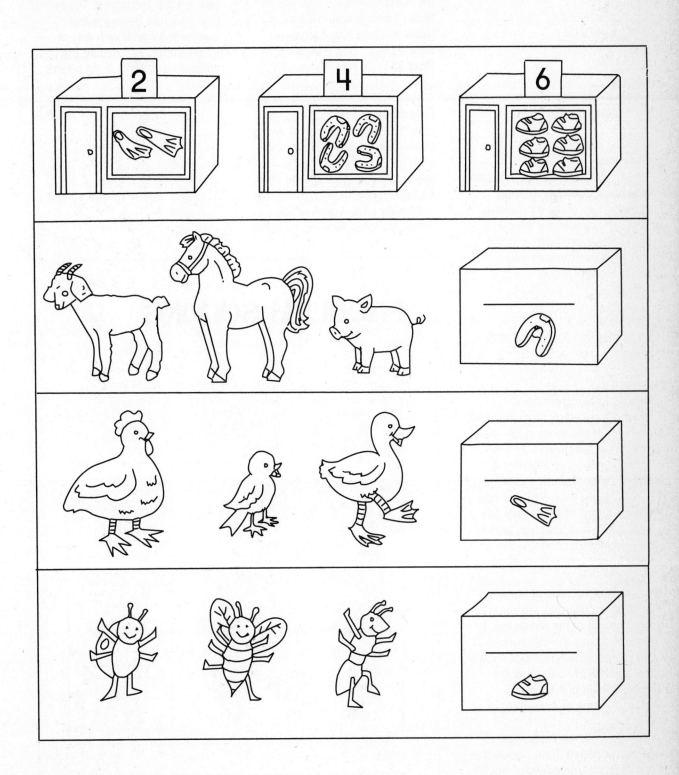

Notes for Home Children identify how many legs the animals have and write the correct number of shoes they need.

Problem Solving and Critical Thinking/**EXPLORING MATHEMATICS** © Scott, Foresman and Company/K Use after pages 63–64.

Use with
Objective 21
    pages 63–64

Focus
Problem Solving
    Use Logical Reasoning

Overview
This activity will provide children with an opportunity to apply strategies to solve a problem. Children will identify the common characteristic in a group and write the number that relates to that group.

Materials
• a large picture of a dog and bird

Teaching Suggestions
Identify the two pictures with the children. Have them study the pictures. **Question:** *Can you name some ways in which a dog is different from a bird?* [A dog is bigger than a bird; it has 4 legs, a bird has 2; a dog has hair, a bird has feathers; and so on.] If needed, continue this activity with other pairs of pictures.
    Distribute copies of Master 21. Direct children's attention to the 3 stores at the top of the page. Discuss the differences in the stores. (Each number shows the number of shoes that the store sells at one time: 2—pairs, 4—sets of 4; 6—sets of 6.)
    Direct children's attention to each row. Have them decide the common characteristic of each group of animals and then write

the number of the store where these animals would shop.
[**Row 1:** Each has 4 legs—4;
Row 2: Each has 2 legs—2;
Row 3: Each has 6 legs—6]

Extension
Distribute two sheets of drawing paper to each child. Have children write a large 6 on one paper and a large 0 on the other paper.
    Provide glue, construction paper, buttons, sequins, or dried

beans for the children. Tell them that they can decorate their numbers 6 and 0 with any of these materials. Display the pictures on a math bulletin board.

CRITICAL THINKING

22

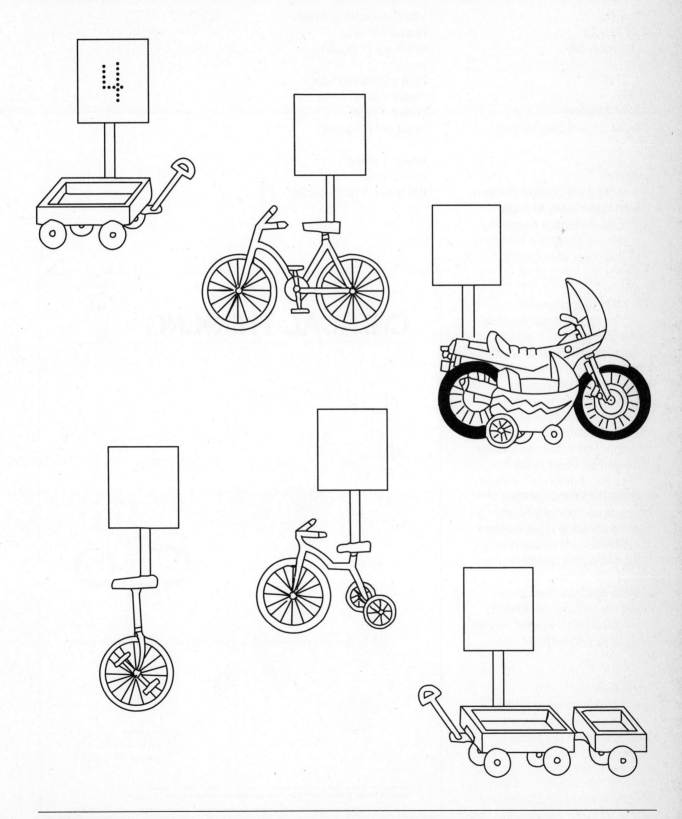

Notes for Home   Children count the wheels on each object and write the number 1 through 6.

Teacher Notes

Use with
Objective 22
   pages 65–66

Focus
Critical Thinking
   Ordering and Sequencing

Overview
This activity will provide children with an opportunity to apply strategies for logical reasoning. Children will analyze a picture to learn the order of numbers.

Teaching Suggestions
Have volunteers write the numbers 0 through 6 in a column on the chalkboard. Next to each numeral, call on other children to draw that many objects. Drawings should be simple.

Distribute copies of Master 22 and direct children's attention to the page. Have children identify each vehicle. Point to the posters with numerals 1 through 6. Explain that the vehicles show the number of wheels, from 1 through 6. Have children count the wheels on each vehicle and write the number on the poster.

When children have completed the activity, ask them to name each vehicle in the correct order from 1 through 6.

Extension
Have children answer riddles that review numbers from 1 through 6. Here are some suggestions.

I have 1 steering wheel.
I have 4 tires.
What am I? [a car]

I have 2 handle bars.
I have 2 tires.
I have 1 seat.
What am I? [a bike]

I have 1 wheel.
I have 1 seat.
What am I? [a unicycle]

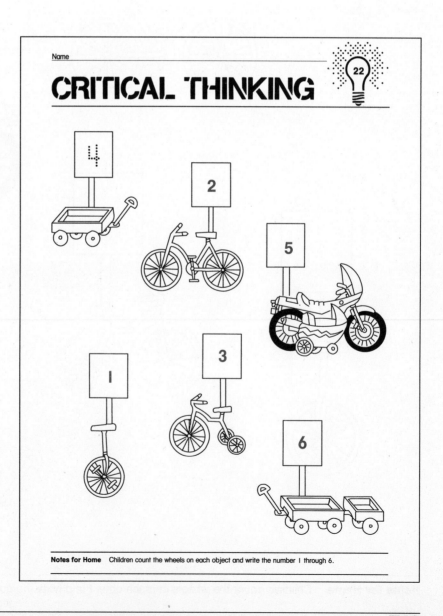

Name

CRITICAL THINKING

22

4

2

5

1

3

6

Notes for Home   Children count the wheels on each object and write the number 1 through 6.

VISUAL THINKING

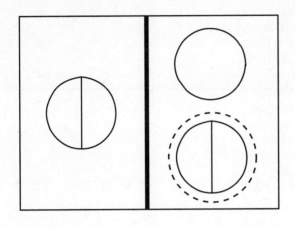

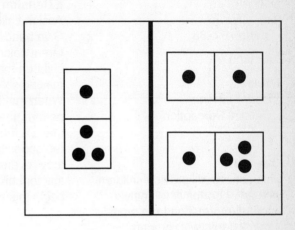

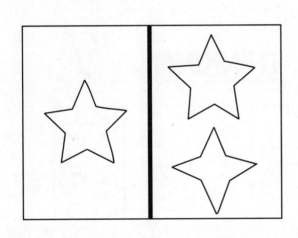

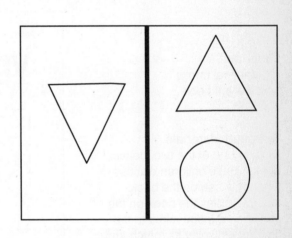

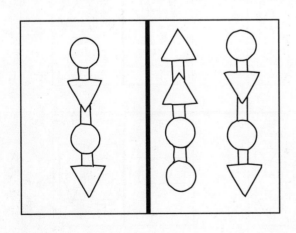

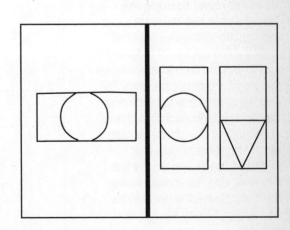

Notes for Home   Children compare designs and then ring the match.

Teacher Notes

Use with
Objective 23
  pages 67–68

Focus
Visual Thinking
  Spatial Perception

Overview
This activity will provide children with an opportunity to analyze and get information from a picture. Children will compare designs to find the one that matches.

Materials
• 2 identical books
• 1 different book

Teaching Materials
Display one of the two identical books. Have children discuss what they see on the book cover. Display the book on the chalkboard ledge. Next to the first book display its match and the different book. **Question:** *Which of these books is the same as the first book?* Repeat the activity with other objects.

  Distribute copies of Master 23 and direct children's attention to the page. Point out the dark line that separates the left side from the right side in each box. Have children find the shape/design on the right-hand side that matches the shape on the left. Children ring the match. Have them complete the page independently. Check each child's activity.

Extension
Assign children to work in pairs. Give beads and counters in different colors to each pair. Tell children that they will take turns making six-object patterns. When the first child has made a pattern, the second child must make a matching pattern from the opposite direction. Then they reverse roles. Demonstrate this for children before they begin this activity.

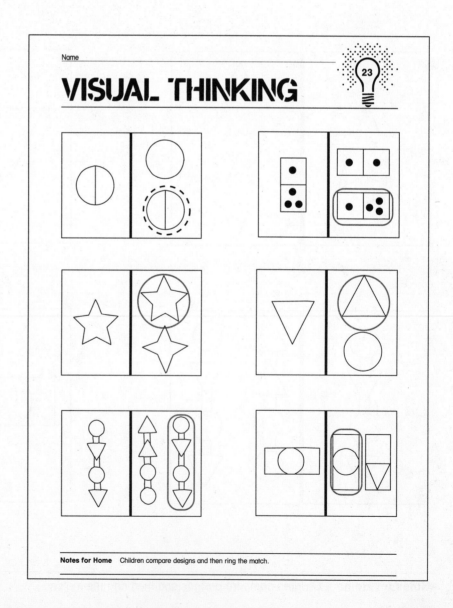

Name _____

VISUAL THINKING

Notes for Home Children compare designs and then ring the match.

VISUAL THINKING

Use with

Objective 24
    pages 69–70

Focus

Visual Thinking
    Spatial Perception

Overview

This activity will provide children with an opportunity to get information from a picture. Children will count objects in a picture.

Materials

• picture of a street scene

Teaching Suggestions

Hold up a large picture of a street scene with groups of objects; houses, cars, children, and so on. Call on volunteers to come up and count the number of houses, cars, children, and so on in the picture.

   Distribute copies of Master 24. Ask children to tell what is happening on the page. Direct children's attention to the rebus pictures at the bottom of the Master. Have a child identify each object. Ask another child to point to the squirrel. Ask how many squirrels there are in the picture. [3] Have them write the number 3 next to the rebus picture of the squirrel. Have children complete the other three rebus pictures.

Extension

Distribute a small portion of clay to each child. Have them try to form the numbers 0 through 6 by working the clay into numerical shapes. After the clay numbers dry, the children can paint them various colors. Children can then put the clay numbers into numerical order 0 through 6.

CRITICAL THINKING

1 __ __ 4 __ __

3   6   2   5

Notes for Home   Children match numbers 1 through 6 in order.

Teacher Notes

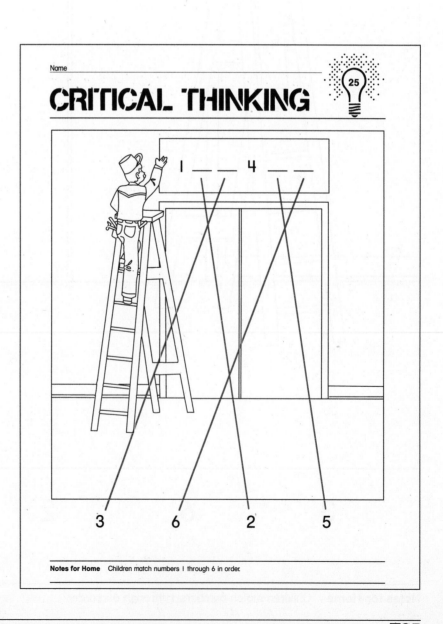

Use with
Objective 25
    pages 73–74

Focus
Critical Thinking
    Ordering and Sequencing

Overview
This critical-thinking activity will provide children with an opportunity to think analytically and logically. Children will determine where elements of the picture belong.

Materials
• number cards 1 through 6

Teaching Suggestions
Display the number cards 1 through 6 in random order. Have children rearrange them in the correct order. Repeat the activity by rearranging the cards.
    Distribute copies of Master 25. Discuss the page with the children. Explain that the elevator man is putting new floor numbers above the elevator. Tell children to draw a line from each number to its correct position. When children have completed the page, draw a similar elevator number panel on the chalkboard. Have volunteers write the missing numbers.

Extension
Tell children that you will tell them a story with numbers in it. Explain that as they listen to the story, they should write the numbers they hear. Here are some suggestions.

    Yesterday 5 children were playing in the park. They had 3 balls and 2 jump ropes. The children had lots of fun.

    I live at 6 Oak Street. On my block there are 2 trees and 3 fire hydrants.

Name _____

CRITICAL THINKING

25

1 __ __ 4 __ __

3   6   2   5

Notes for Home   Children match numbers 1 through 6 in order.

CRITICAL THINKING

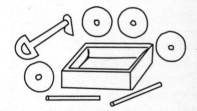

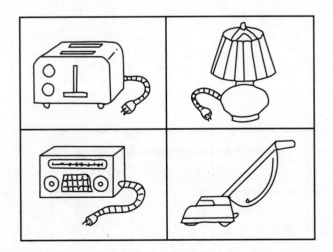

Notes for Home   Children use picture clues to mark an X on the correct object.

Use with
Objective 26
   page 75

Focus
Critical Thinking
   Using Logic

Overview
This critical-thinking activity will provide children with an opportunity to think analytically and logically. Children will determine the object being made.

Materials
• chalk
• paint jar
• paintbrush

Teaching Suggestions
Explain that people often do and say things that can help others figure out what will happen next. Pick up a piece of chalk and walk to the chalkboard. *Question: What do you think will happen next?* [You will print or draw something on the chalkboard.] Have children explain why they made this prediction. Explain that picking up the chalk and walking to the chalkboard are clues that can help them predict what will happen next. Then pick up a paint jar and a paintbrush. *Question: What do you think will happen next?* [You will paint a picture.]

Distribute copies of Master 26. Direct children's attention to the woman at the workbench. Explain that the materials below the carpenter are clues as to what she will be making. Point out the completed objects in the

boxes below each set of materials. Explain to children that they have to use the clues to decide which object she will make with the materials. Tell them to mark an X on those objects. Call on volunteers to explain their answers.

Extension
Explain to children that you will tell them some riddles. Have them listen for clues that will help them get the answers.

Call on volunteers to give the answers and identify the clues that they used to get the correct answer.

I'm soft and fluffy.
   You put your head on me to sleep or rest.
   What am I? [pillow]

I'm made of wood.
   I have black and white keys.
   You play music on me.
   What am I? [piano]

Name _____

CRITICAL THINKING

26

Notes for Home   Children use picture clues to mark an X on the correct object.

DECISION MAKING

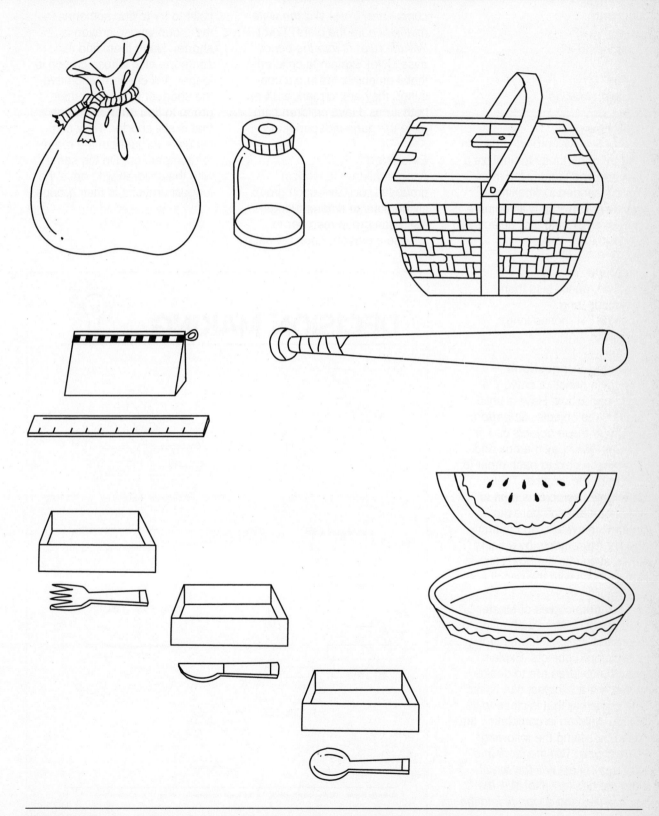

Notes for Home Children identify objects that can fit into containers by marking an X on both of them.

Use with
Objective 27
   pages 85–86

Focus
Decision Making

Overview
This activity will provide children with an opportunity to analyze a problem and identify the information needed for making a decision. Children will compare the length or height of objects in a picture.

Materials
• crayon, pencil less than
   8 inches long
• box (8 - 11 inches long)
• a ruler

Teaching Suggestions
Display a pencil, a crayon, a ruler, and a box. Have a child identify the objects. **Question:** *Which of these objects can fit into the box?* Lay the box and the crayon next to each other to compare the lengths. Then stand the two objects next to each other to compare the heights. Have a child confirm the measurements by placing the crayon into the box. Repeat the process with the pencil and the ruler.

   Distribute copies of Master 27 and direct children's attention to the page. Help children identify the pictured objects. Explain that the children are to decide whether each object can fit into the container that is close to it. Guide children in completing the page by asking the following: **Questions:** *Will the jar fit into the bag?* [Yes] *Will the bat fit into the basket?* [No] *Will the fork, knife, and spoon fit into the*

containers? [Yes] *Will the watermelon fit onto the plate?* [Yes] *Will the ruler fit into the pencil case?* [No] Explain to children that if an object fits into a container, they are to mark an X on both items. Have children complete the page independently.

Extension
Assign children to work in groups of six. Give each group six crayons of different lengths. Ask each group member to choose a crayon. Then tell each

child to try to find someone in the group whose crayon is shorter. Have them find someone else whose crayon is longer. Tell children who have the shortest crayons in their group to find another crayon that is still shorter. They can circulate throughout the room for comparison. Do the same with the children who have the longest crayons in their groups.

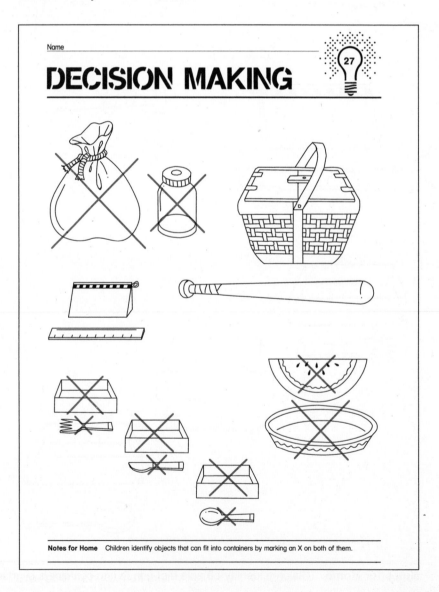

Name _____

DECISION MAKING

27

Notes for Home   Children identify objects that can fit into containers by marking an X on both of them.

CRITICAL THINKING

Notes for Home Children identify the spectators from shortest to tallest by writing a 1, 2, 3 order.

Use with
Objective 28
    pages 87–88

Focus
Critical Thinking
    Classifying and Sorting

Overview
This activity will provide children with an opportunity to think analytically and logically. Children will sort objects according to height.

Teaching Suggestions
Call on three children to stand in front of the class. Arrange the children in order of height, from shortest to tallest. Then have them rearrange themselves from tallest to shortest.

   Distribute copies of Master 28. Tell children that the people in the picture are watching a parade. Point out the four groups of family members.
Question: How should each family arrange themselves so that all of them can see the parade? Have the children point to a group of three spectators. Explain to the children that they have to decide where the spectators in each group of three should stand. Tell children to put a number 1 above the shortest person. Put a 2 above the next tallest and a 3 above the tallest person in each group. Call on volunteers to explain their answers.

Extension
Ask children to draw a picture that contains a mountain, a building, and a person. Have them decide which is the tallest and which is the shortest before they begin to draw. Call on volunteers to show and tell about their pictures using the words <u>tallest</u> and <u>shortest</u>.

Name _____

CRITICAL THINKING

Notes for Home   Children identify the spectators from shortest to tallest by writing a 1, 2, 3 order.

DECISION MAKING

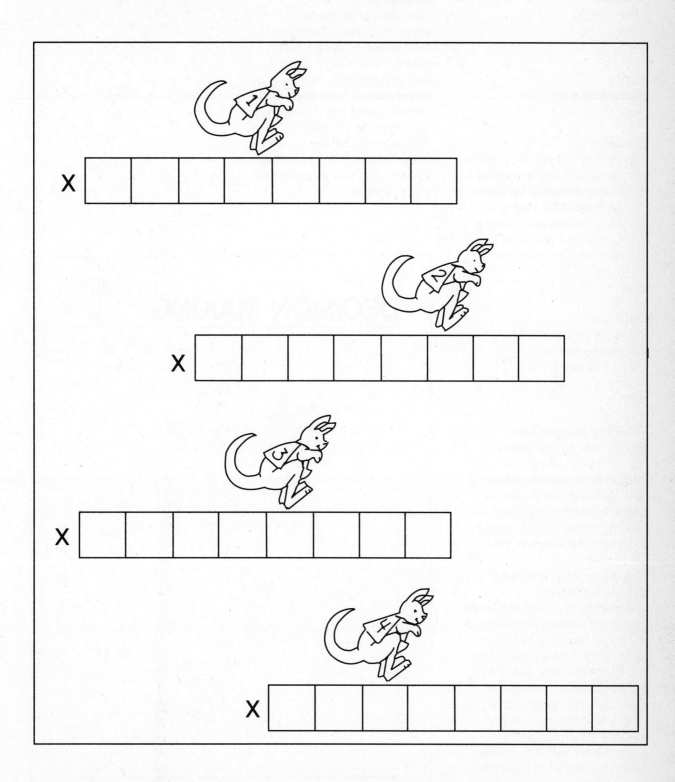

Notes for Home   Children learn about units of measure by coloring the units that show each kangaroo jump.
Then they ring the kangaroo that has jumped the farthest.

Problem Solving and Critical Thinking/**EXPLORING MATHEMATICS** © Scott, Foresman and Company/K   Use after pages 89–90.

Use with
Objective 29
   pages 89–90

Focus
Decision Making

Overview
This activity will provide children with an opportunity to analyze a problem and identify the information needed for making a decision. Children will interpret information in a picture to find the best answer to a given question.

Materials
• chalk or tape
• 6 building blocks (about 6" long)
• crayons

Teaching Suggestions
Using chalk or tape, make a "Starting Line" on the classroom floor. Call on several children to take standing jumps from the line. After each child's jump, lay building blocks edge to edge to determine the length of the jump. Keep score on the chalkboard. Name the child who jumped the farthest.

Distribute copies of Master 29 and direct children's attention to the page. Ask them to look at the four kangaroos. Have children color the units that show the length of each kangaroo jump. Tell children to decide which kangaroo jumped the farthest. Which kangaroo jumped the least? Ask children to ring the winner of the contest.

Extension
Take children to the gym or playground. Have them practice for a throwing contest. Designate a marked area, starting line, and goal line. Provide 4 different colored bean bags. Have children take turns throwing a bean bag toward the goal line. After each round, decide who threw the bean bag the farthest. Children can play this game in groups of four.

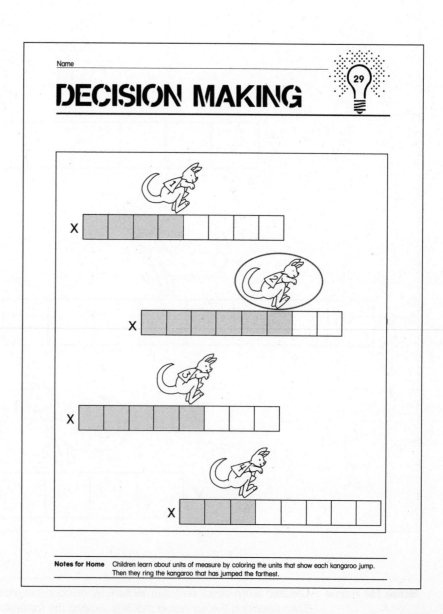

Name _____

DECISION MAKING

Notes for Home Children learn about units of measure by coloring the units that show each kangaroo jump. Then they ring the kangaroo that has jumped the farthest.

PROBLEM SOLVING

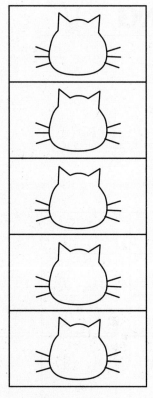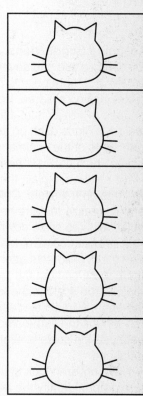

Notes for Home   Children color a picture graph by comparing objects on a scale. Then they ring the heaviest object.

Teacher Notes

Use with
Objective 30
   pages 91–92

Focus
Problem Solving
   Make a Graph

Overview
The problem-solving activity will provide children with an opportunity to select and apply learned strategies. Children will make a graph of pictorial information and will analyze the information.

Materials
• balance scale
• classroom objects

Teaching Suggestions
Display a scale and several small classroom objects on a table. Call on children, in turn, to choose two objects of different weights. Place each on separate sides of the scale and discover which object is heavier. Have children explain the weights on the scale. Children should realize that the heavier object tilts the scale down.

   Distribute copies of Master 30 and direct children's attention to the page. Point out the two kittens on the scale at the top of the page. Explain that each kitten weighs the same amount because the scale is evenly balanced.

   Have children look at the picture graph. Identify the animals at the bottom of each column. Point to the kitten faces in the first column. *Question: How much did one kitten weigh?* [the same as the other kitten] Tell children to color in one kitten face at the bottom of the column

because one kitten weighs the same as one kitten. Point to the picture of the scale with the dog and two kittens. *Question: How much does the dog weigh?* [the same as 2 kittens] Have children put a finger on the dog pictured in the second column of the graph. *Question: How many boxes should be filled in above the dog?* [2] Have children color the rest of the picture graph independently. Then ask children to ring the picture of the animal on the graph who weighs

the most. [calf] Check each child's activity.

Extension
Distribute two sheets of drawing paper to each child. Have children draw a picture of an object or animal that is heavy. Then have them draw an object or animal that is lighter. Call on volunteers to show and tell about the differences in weight.

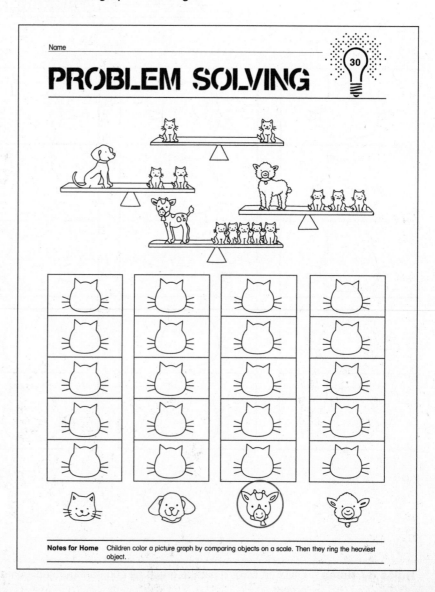

Name _____

PROBLEM SOLVING

Notes for Home   Children color a picture graph by comparing objects on a scale. Then they ring the heaviest object.

CRITICAL THINKING

MILK

Notes for Home   Children ring objects that can be counted and objects that are used to measure liquids.

Problem Solving and Critical Thinking/EXPLORING MATHEMATICS © Scott, Foresman and Company/K   Use after pages 93–94.

Teacher Notes

Use with
Objective 31
    pages 93–94

Focus
Critical Thinking
    Classifying and Sorting

Overview
This activity will provide children with an opportunity to think analytically and logically. Children sort objects and ring those that are counted and those that are used to measure liquid amounts.

Materials
• 6 counters
• a pint container full of water
• 2 1-cup measures

Teaching Suggestions
Display the 6 counters on a table. **Questions:** *Could you pour these counters?* [no] *Would you weigh these counters?* [no] *What would you do to find the number of counters?* [count]

Then display the pint container of water and the 1-cup measure. **Questions:** *What is in this container?* [water] *Can I find out how much water is inside by counting the drops?* [No] *How would you find the amount of water in this container?* [Pour it into the cup measure] Pour the water into the cup measure and tell children that there are 2 cups of water in the container.

Distribute copies of Master 31. Have children identify the objects in the top box. [strawberries, carrots, potatoes, and a container of milk] Explain that

some of these objects can be counted. Tell children to ring the objects in the box that can be counted. Then have children identify the pictures in the bottom box. [measuring cup, spoon, tea cup, and a bunch of bananas] Ask children to ring the objects that are used to measure amounts of liquid such as water, milk, juice and so on. Review the page with the children. Encourage them to suggest other examples for each group.

Extension
Distribute magazines, drawing paper, scissors, and paste to the children. Have each child find two pictures of things that can be counted and two pictures of things that either measure liquids or are things that must be poured to be measured. Ask children to show and tell about their pictures.

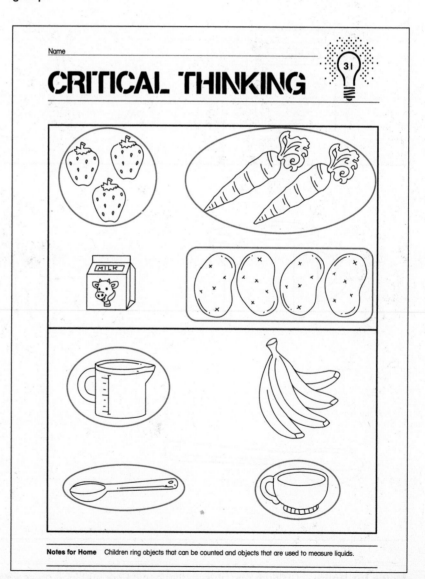

Name _____

CRITICAL THINKING 31

Notes for Home   Children ring objects that can be counted and objects that are used to measure liquids.

VISUAL THINKING

Notes for Home Children complete patterns and color the circles red and the squares blue. Then they make their own pattern.

Problem Solving and Critical Thinking/**EXPLORING MATHEMATICS** © Scott, Foresman and Company/**K**   Use after pages 95–96.

32

Teacher Notes

Use with
Objective 32
   pages 95–96

Focus
Visual Thinking
   Spatial Perception

Overview
This visual-thinking activity will provide children with an opportunity to make their own patterns using squares and circles.

Materials
• red and blue crayons

Teaching Suggestions
Draw the following on the chalkboard:

Ask a volunteer to find a circle and draw a line under it. Ask another volunteer to find a square and draw an X on it. Continue in this manner with the remaining circles and squares. Explain to the children that they are following a pattern of shapes.
   Distribute copies of Master 32. Direct children's attention to the page. Have children complete the patterns on the Master. After the patterns are completed, have the children color the circles red and the squares blue. At the bottom half of the Master, have children create their own circle and square patterns. They can exchange their pattern with a neighbor to see if they can follow the sequence.

Extension
Distribute magazines, drawing paper, scissors, and paste to the children. Ask children to cut out pictures from magazines of objects that are shaped like circles or squares. Have them make a pattern with their cut-outs. Create a bulletin board display with the pictures.

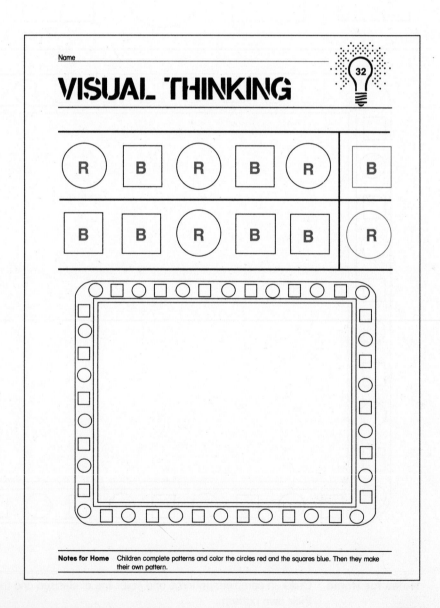

VISUAL THINKING

33

Notes for Home   Children find and color the triangles yellow and the rectangles green.

Problem Solving and Critical Thinking/**EXPLORING MATHEMATICS** © Scott, Foresman and Company/K   Use after pages 97–98.

Teacher Notes

Use with
Objective 33
    pages 97–98

Focus
Visual Thinking
    Spatial Perception

Overview
This activity will provide children with an opportunity to make judgments on spatial relationships. Children will find and color the triangles and rectangles in a picture.

Materials
• yellow and green crayons
• punchout triangles and rectangles
• triangular and rectangular objects

Teaching Suggestions
Give each child one punchout triangle and one punchout rectangle. Display different circular and triangular objects to the children. Have children hold up the punchout shape that matches the shape of the object that is being held up in front of the class.

Distribute copies of Master 33. Discuss the page with the children. Tell children to find the triangles and rectangles in the picture of outer space. Have them color the triangles yellow and the rectangles green.

Extension
Assign children to work in groups of eight. Take children to the school gym. Have each group arrange themselves in a rectangle; then a triangle. Play a record or tape when the children change positions. Use the rhythm of the music as the time to move to a different position in the shape. Continue the activity by reassigning groups.

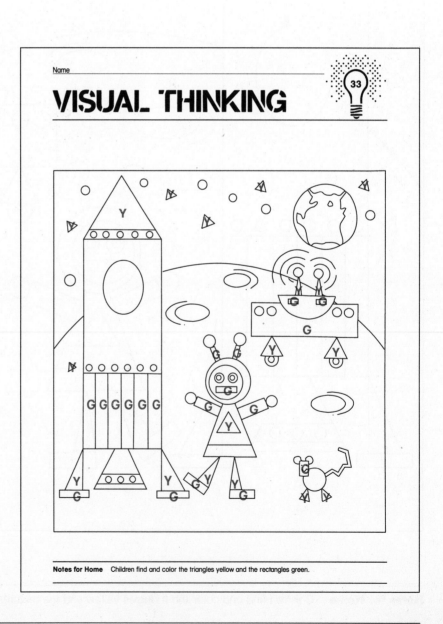

Name _____

VISUAL THINKING

Notes for Home Children find and color the triangles yellow and the rectangles green.

34

VISUAL THINKING

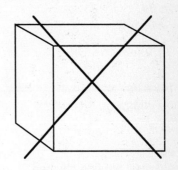

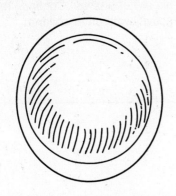

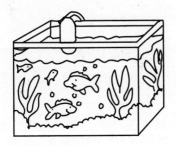

Notes for Home   Children ring objects shaped like a ball and mark an X on the objects shaped like a box.

Teacher Notes

Use with

Objective 34
   pages 99–100

Focus

Visual Thinking
   Visual Patterns

Overview

This activity will provide children with an opportunity to make judgments about shapes. Children ring objects shaped like a ball and mark an X on objects shaped like a box.

Materials

• several different kinds of balls and boxes

Teaching Suggestions

Hold up each ball, one at a time, and call on volunteers to describe it. Pass the balls around to the children so they can examine each ball closely. Repeat the activity with the boxes.

   Direct children's attention to Master 34. Have the objects at the top of the page identified. [ball, box] Tell children to look at the black line around the ball and the black X on the box. Look at the pictures on the rest of the page. Have those pictures identified and ask a volunteer what he or she thinks should be done with the rest of the page. (Ring the objects shaped like a ball; mark an X on the objects shaped like a box) Have children complete the page independently. Call on volunteers to show and explain their answers.

Extension

Place six objects of different shapes in a large bag, such as building blocks, alphabet blocks, a shoe box taped closed, food cans, empty soft drink cans, rubber balls, styrofoam balls, and oranges. Call on a child to cover his or her eyes, reach into the bag, and feel one object. Have the child tell whether the object is a ball, box, or can. Then ask the child to take the object out of the bag to check

his or her answer. Continue the activity with other children.

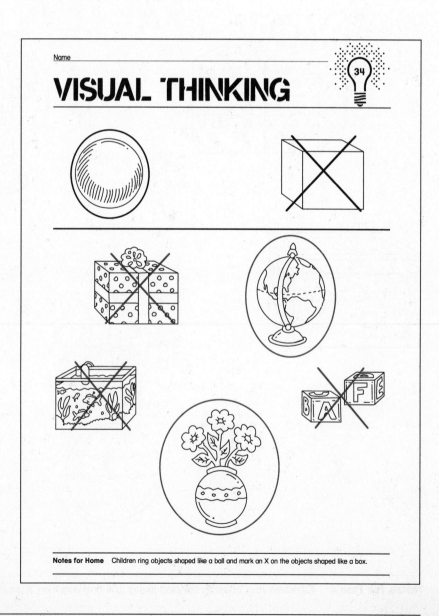

PROBLEM SOLVING

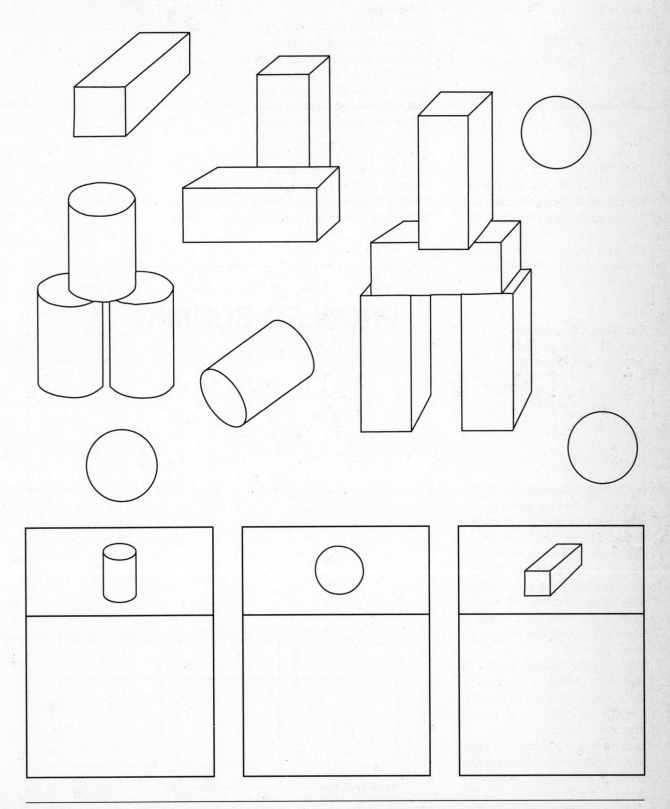

Notes for Home   Children identify objects and count them. Then they enter the information in a table.

Problem Solving and Critical Thinking/**EXPLORING MATHEMATICS** © Scott, Foresman and Company/K   Use after pages 101–102.

Use with
Objective 35
  pages 101–102

Focus
Problem Solving
  Make a Table

Overview
This activity will provide children with an opportunity to select and apply appropriate strategies to solve a problem. Children identify objects that belong in given groups, count them, and enter the information in a table.

Teaching Suggestions
On the chalkboard draw a table similar to the following:

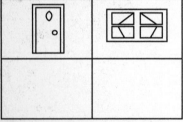

(Note: If your classroom has more than six of either of these, substitute another classroom feature, limited to six examples.) Identify the pictures with the children. Then help them count the number of doors and windows in the classroom. Have volunteers record the numbers in the table.

   Distribute copies of Master 35 and direct children's attention to the page. Have children identify the types of objects pictured in the table. They are to count each object and record the total in the table independently. Call on volunteers to explain their answers.

Extension
Have children do a five-minute Shapes Survey of the classroom. On the chalkboard draw a table with the three headings as shown on Master 35 (can, ball, and box). Ask children to point out all the objects in the room shaped like a can, a ball, and a box. Keep a tally of their suggestions. At the end of five minutes, count the number of objects suggested for each category and enter that figure into the table.

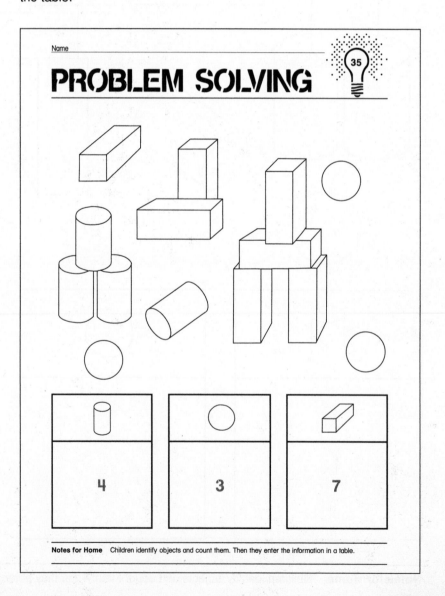

Name _____

PROBLEM SOLVING

| 4 | 3 | 7 |

Notes for Home   Children identify objects and count them. Then they enter the information in a table.

VISUAL THINKING

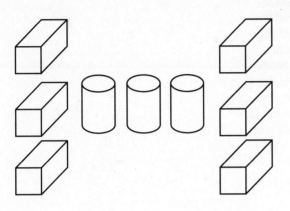

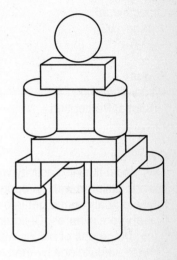

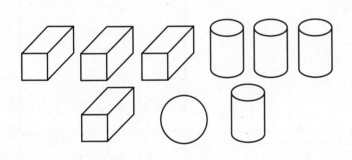

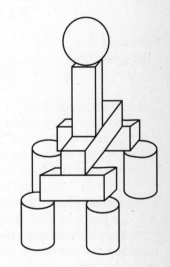

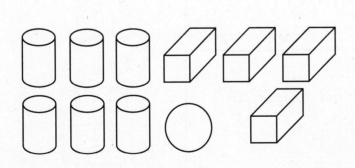

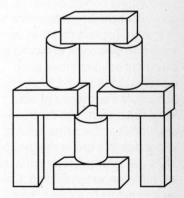

Notes for Home   Children match each set of blocks with the building on the right.

Use with
Objective 36
  page 103

Focus
Visual Thinking
  Spatial Perception

Overview
This visual-thinking activity will provide children with an opportunity to analyze and get information from pictures. Children compare groups of blocks with completed buildings by matching each group to the building.

Materials
• building blocks

Teaching Suggestions
Use a set of building blocks to make a building. Have the children study the building carefully. Have them identify the shapes of blocks. Ask them to tell how many of each shape are used to build the building. Then take the building apart and have volunteers sort the blocks into groups by shapes and/or size. Count the blocks in each group.

Distribute copies of Master 36 and direct children's attention to the page. Explain that they are to decide which set of blocks at the left is used to make each building at the right. Children can count the shapes of each kind. Have them find the building that uses the same amount of shapes that are in the group. They are to draw a line connecting each set to its building. Call on volunteers to explain their answers.

Extension
Assign children to work in groups of three. Give each group ten blocks of different shapes and sizes. Challenge each group to design one building using all their blocks. Discuss each group's building in terms of design, height, and use of the blocks. Combine the different buildings to make a city.

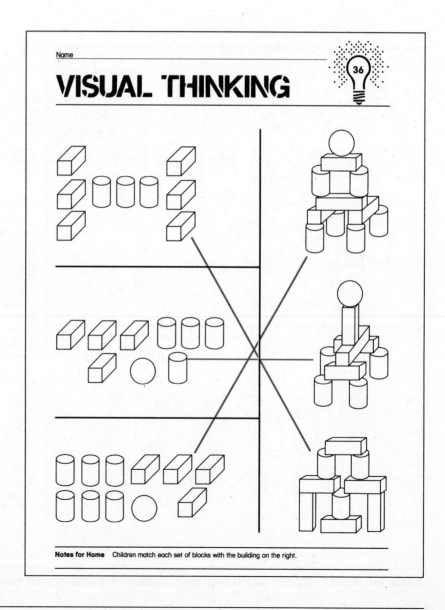

Name _____

VISUAL THINKING

36

Notes for Home   Children match each set of blocks with the building on the right.

CRITICAL THINKING

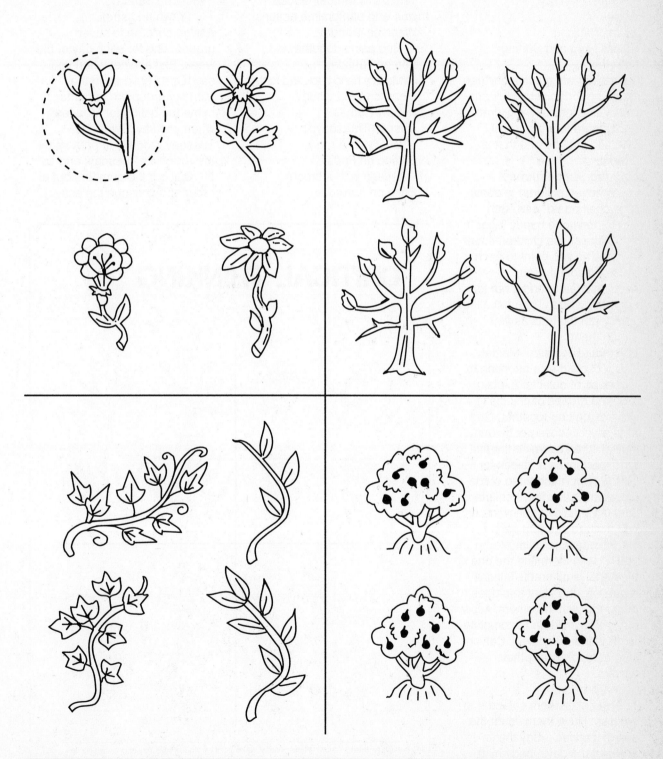

Notes for Home Children compare groups of objects to find one that is different. They ring the object that does not belong.

Problem Solving and Critical Thinking/**EXPLORING MATHEMATICS** © Scott, Foresman and Company/**K**   Use after pages 111–112.

Teacher Notes

Use with
Objective 37
pages 111–112

Focus
Critical Thinking
Classifying and Sorting

Overview
This activity will provide children with an opportunity to think analytically and logically. Children will compare four groups of objects to find the one that is different.

Teaching Suggestions
Call on seven children to come to the chalkboard. Ask each child to draw one happy face. Then have all the children count the faces as you point to each one. Ask another group of seven children to add a hat to each happy face. Then have the class count the hats as you point to them.

Distribute copies of Master 37. Direct children's attention to the groups of objects. Explain that three groups of objects in each box belong together. One of the objects does not belong. Have children examine the first of the four boxes and look for some way in which three of the objects are alike. Have children count the petals, and flowers on each plant to see that each plant has seven similar elements. Have them find the one object that is different. Tell children to ring the plant that does not belong with the others. Allow time for the children to complete the page independently. Call on volunteers to explain their answers.

Extension
Show the classroom calendar to the class. Have them count the days of the week. Say the names of the days, beginning with Monday, and ask children to repeat them.

Teach this Mother Goose rhyme with pantomime actions.
Wash on Monday,
  (Rub palms together.)
Iron on Tuesday,
  (Move a hand back and forth.)
Mend on Wednesday,
  (Sew clothes.)
Dust on Thursday,
  (Dust with a rag.)
Sweep on Friday,
  (Sweep with a broom.)
Bake on Saturday,
  (Mix batter; put cookies in the oven.)
  Rest on Sunday,
    (Yawn and stretch.)
Assign children to seven groups, one for each day of the week. Explain that when you say "One," children in the Monday group are to pantomime the action for Monday; when you say "Two," the Tuesday group is to pantomime the action for Tuesday; and so on. Call out the numbers out of order and continue the activity.

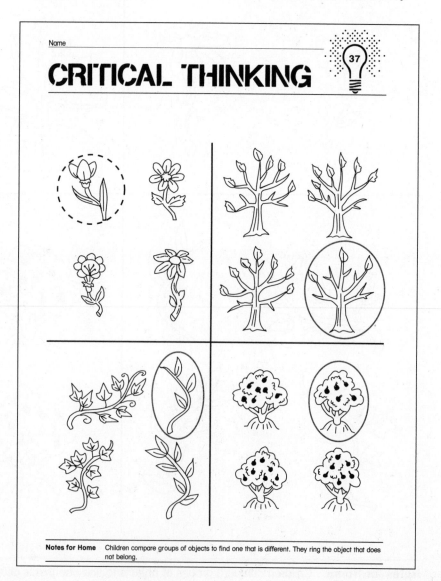

Name _____

CRITICAL THINKING

37

Notes for Home   Children compare groups of objects to find one that is different. They ring the object that does not belong.

CRITICAL THINKING

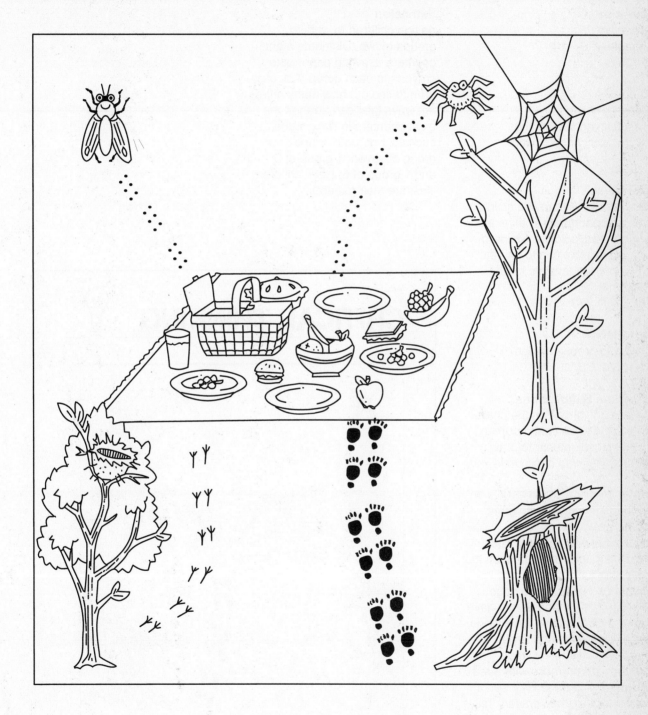

Notes for Home   Children use visual clues to find the footprints. They color the fly footprints trail green and color the spider footprints trail red.

Use with
Objective 38
    pages 113–114

Focus
Critical Thinking
    Explaining Reasoning
    and Justifying Answers

Overview
This activity will provide children with an opportunity to think analytically and logically. Children will use visual clues to find the character responsible for the footprints.

Materials
• red and green crayons

Teaching Suggestions
Draw eight circles on the chalkboard and have them counted. Then ask volunteers to draw eight dots inside each circle.

Repeat the activity with other pictures.

Distribute copies of Master 38. Direct children's attention to the page. Point out Fly and Spider at the top of the page. Explain that Fly and Spider have found a picnic. They have made tracks on the ground to get there. Tell children to trace Spider's set of tracks with a red crayon and to trace Fly's set of tracks with a green crayon. Tell them to count the footprints of the other animals. Help them find the animal that walks with eight legs. Call on volunteers to explain their choices.

Extension
Assign children to work in groups of two. Distribute eight counters, drawing paper, and crayons to each group. Ask children to find out how many different ways they can arrange the eight counters in two groups, such as 1 group of 1 and 1 group of seven, 1 group of 2 and 1 group of 6. Have children illustrate their patterns.

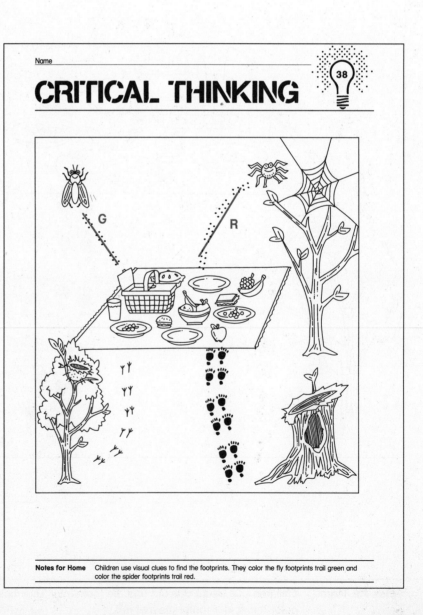

Name _____

CRITICAL THINKING

38

G   R

Notes for Home   Children use visual clues to find the footprints. They color the fly footprints trail green and color the spider footprints trail red.

PROBLEM SOLVING

Notes for Home   Children identify groups of 7 and 8. Then they record the groups of items in the table.

Problem Solving and Critical Thinking/**EXPLORING MATHEMATICS** © Scott, Foresman and Company/K   Use after pages 115–116.

Use with

Objective 39
   pages 115–116

Focus

Problem Solving
   Make a Table

Overview

This problem-solving activity will provide children with an opportunity to use information from a picture to make a table. Children will count specific items pictured and record the data in a table.

Materials

• 7 crayons
• 8 sheets of paper

Teaching Suggestions

Hold up 7 crayons. Have children count each crayon with you. Ask two children to write the number 7 on the chalkboard. Repeat this activity using 8 sheets of paper. Continue with other items in groups of seven or eight as necessary.

   Direct children's attention to Master 39. Have children look at the big picture. Discuss what they see. Look at the small pictures in the boxes at the bottom in the table. Have children identify the pictures shown in the boxes. Tell children that they are to look at the picture in each box. They are to count how many of the same things they see in the big picture, and then write the number in each box in the table. Have children complete the page independently and then color it. Call on volunteers to show their work and explain their answers.

Extension

Give magazines, scissors, paste, and drawing paper to the children. Demonstrate how to fold the paper in half horizontally. Tell children to write the number 7 at the top of the box on the left and the number 8 at the top of the box on the right. Have children cut and paste items from the magazines to show the number they have written in each box. Display the pictures on a bulletin board.

VISUAL THINKING

Use with
Objective 40
  pages 117–118

Focus
Visual Thinking
  Visual Patterns

Overview
This visual-thinking activity will provide children with experience in analyzing and getting information from pictures. Children compare patterns to a model and will find the pattern that is similar.

Materials
• 9 paper circles for each child

Teaching Suggestions
Distribute 9 paper circles to each child. On the chalkboard draw the following designs:

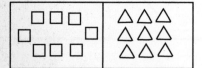

Ask children to count the objects. Have children use their circles to create the same group of objects at their desk. They may tell how many circles they used. Repeat the activity with the triangles.

Direct children's attention to Master 40. Point out that there are three rows of patterns or designs. Have children point to the triangle pattern in the first box of the top row and tell how many objects they see. Then have children look at the other groups of shape patterns in the

row and point to the group that is similar to the pattern in the first box. Tell children to ring that group. Have children complete the rest of the page independently. Have them explain their answers by counting the items.

Extension
Distribute magazines, scissors, drawing paper, and paste to the children. Have them cut out two different groups of 9 items each. Tell children to cut out items that

have similar characteristics for each group. Some examples are animals, cars, vegetables, or people. Have children paste them on the paper. Let children show and tell about their work.

Name _____

VISUAL THINKING

Notes for Home Children compare patterns. They ring the pattern that is similar to the one in each box.

CRITICAL THINKING

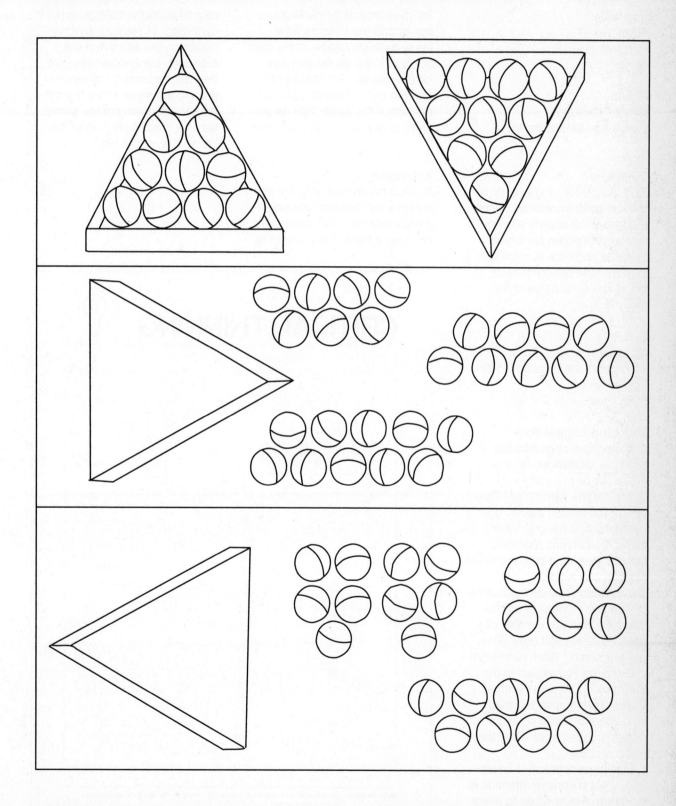

Notes for Home   Children identify the contents of an open box to determine the number of items in closed boxes of the same size.

Problem Solving and Critical Thinking/**EXPLORING MATHEMATICS** © Scott, Foresman and Company/**K**   Use after pages 119–120.

Use with

Objective 41
    pages 119–120

Focus

Critical Thinking
    Making Generalizations

Overview

This critical-thinking activity will provide children with an opportunity to think analytically and logically. Children generalize from the contents of open boxes to determine the number of items in a closed box of the same size.

Materials

• 3 or more identical boxes of crayons

Teaching Suggestions

Display three closed boxes of crayons. **Question:** *How do these boxes compare in size?* [They are the same size.] Open one of the boxes, display the contents, and have children count the crayons together. Open the second box and count the crayons inside it. **Questions:** *How do the number of crayons in the second box compare with the number of crayons in the first box?* [They are the same.] *What number of crayons do you expect in the third box?* [The same amount.] Ask a child to open the third box. Have children count its contents together to verify their generalization.

Distribute copies of Master 41. Direct children's attention to the page. Ask children to examine the contents of the first two boxes and then decide how many balls should be in the third box. Let them do the last row independently. Tell children to ring the correct set of balls and then color the page. Call on volunteers to explain their answers.

Extension

Have children work in pairs to create their own generalizing demonstration. Give each pair two paper bags. Tell children to decide on some objects to put in each bag. Make sure children duplicate the items and the amounts. Let children present their paper bags for other children to examine. Have the others tell how many of the same items a third paper bag of the same size would hold.

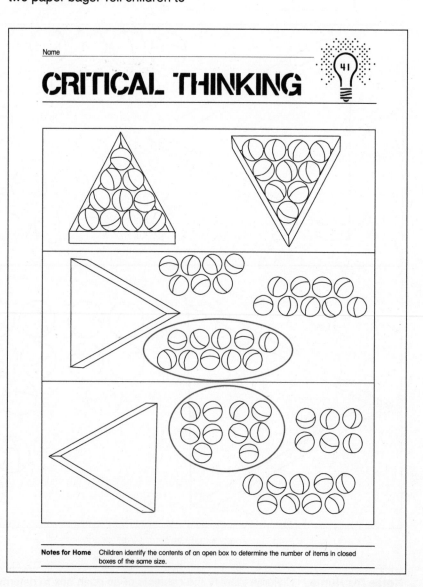

VISUAL THINKING

42

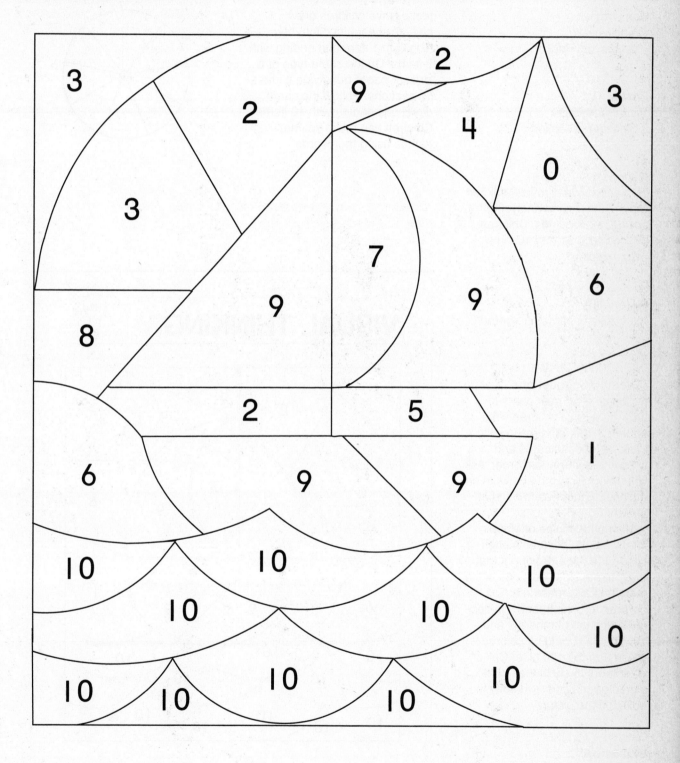

Notes for Home   Children identify the numbers 9 and 10. Then they color the 9s green and the 10s blue to find a hidden picture.

Use with
Objective 42
  pages 121–122

Focus
Visual Thinking
  Spatial Perception

Overview
This activity will provide children with experience in analyzing spatial relationships. Children will color the 9s and 10s in a hidden picture.

Materials
• large index cards numbered
  0 to 9

Teaching Suggestions
Display the number cards in order and have children write each number as you show the card. Shuffle the cards and show them in random order. Ask volunteers to name and write on a piece of paper each number shown.

Distribute copies of Master 42. Direct the children's attention to the page. Point out that each of the small sections of the page has a number in it. Tell children to color in only the sections with the numbers 9 and 10. The 9s should be colored green and the 10s blue. Call on volunteers to show their completed pages and to identify the object in the picture.

Extension
Give children crayons and a large circular piece of paper that has been divided into 9 sec-

tions. Have children draw objects in each section, beginning with 1 item and ending with 9 items. Do the same type of a circular paper but divide it into 10 sections. Follow the same directions ending with 10 items. Children can make spinner games using their cards.

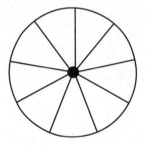

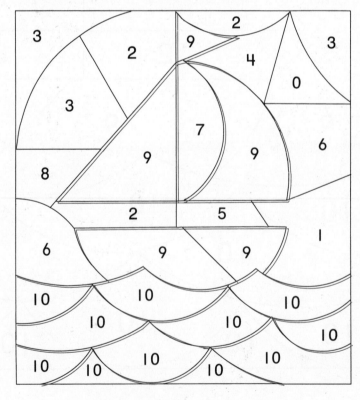

Name _____

VISUAL THINKING

Notes for Home Children identify the numbers 9 and 10. Then they color the 9s green and the 10s blue to find a hidden picture.

DECISION MAKING

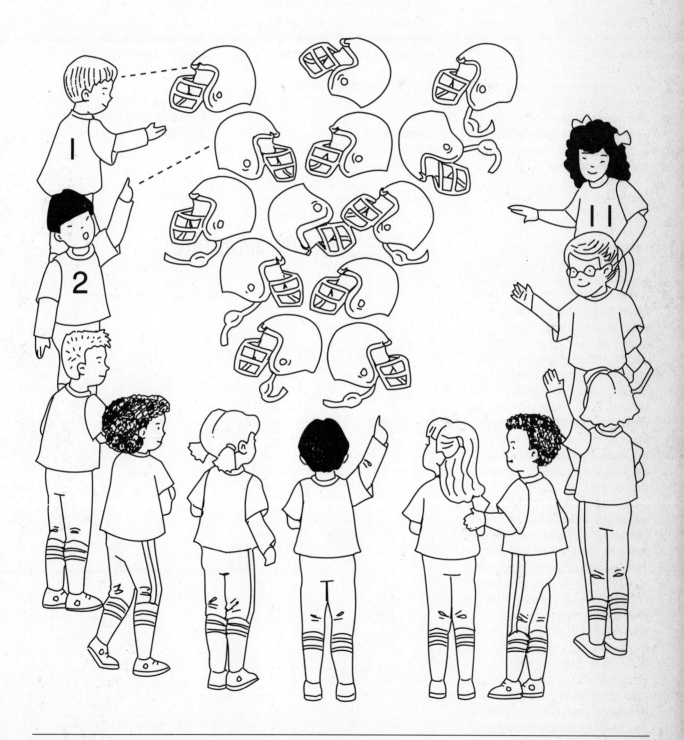

43

Notes for Home Children match helmets by drawing a line to each player. Then they number each shirt and draw Xs on helmets that are not needed.

Teacher Notes

Use with

Objective 43
   pages 123–124

Focus

Decision Making

Overview

This activity will provide children with an opportunity to analyze a problem and to identify information needed for making a decision. Children match helmets with players to determine how many are needed.

Materials

• 11 counters

Teaching Suggestions

Tell children that you are holding several counters and they must discover how many. Have them close their eyes. Explain that you will drop the counters one at a time as they listen to each sound. Drop the counters slowly. Ask volunteers to report how many they heard. Remind them to keep their eyes closed as you drop the counters a second time. This time have children count aloud in order to keep track of the number of counters dropped.

   Distribute copies of Master 43. Direct children's attention to the page. Talk about the picture with the children. ***Questions: How many players are shown in this picture? How do you know?*** [Children should reason that they see numbers on some of the children. The highest number is 11, and it is on the last child.] Ask children, without counting, if they think there are enough helmets for each child. Ask them what they could do to find out if there are enough hel-

mets. [Match a helmet to each player.] Have children draw a line from each helmet to a player. Tell children to put an X on any helmet that is not needed. Then tell them to continue the numbers in order by writing a number on each child's back who does not have one. Have children complete the page independently.

Extension

Present these riddles to the children. Have them listen to the clues and give answers. You may wish to display a number line or number cards in sequential order for children to use with this activity.

   I am more than 10.
   I am one less than 12.
   Who am I? [11]

   I am less than 12.
   I am two more than 9.
   Who am I? [11]

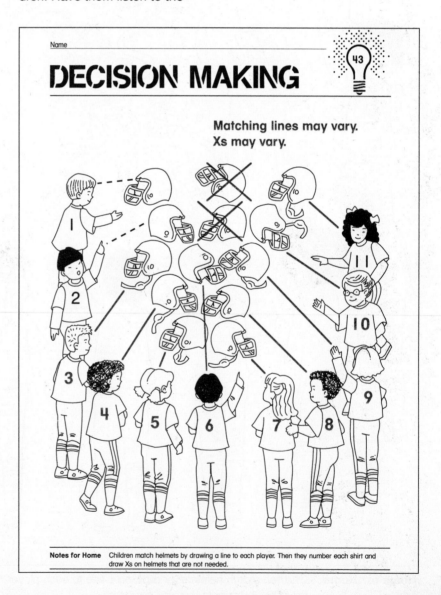

Name _____

DECISION MAKING (43)

Matching lines may vary.
Xs may vary.

Notes for Home   Children match helmets by drawing a line to each player. Then they number each shirt and draw Xs on helmets that are not needed.

CRITICAL THINKING

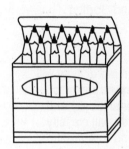

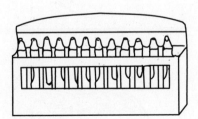

Notes for Home   Children identify and ring packages of 12.

Use with
Objective 44
    pages 125–126

Focus
Critical Thinking
    Classifying and Sorting

Overview
This critical-thinking activity will provide children with an opportunity to think analytically and logically. Children will classify objects according to quantities of twelve.

Materials
• empty egg carton
• muffin tin that holds 4 or 8

Teaching Suggestions
Discuss experiences that the children have had on shopping trips with their parents.
Questions: *Are all the packages in the store the same size?* [No] *Does every package hold the same number of things?* [No] Display an egg carton. Have children count the cups.
Question: *How many eggs are usually sold in one package?* [12] Display the muffin tin. Have children count the cups in the tin. ***Question:*** *How many muffins would be in a package of this size?* Invite children to tell about items they know are sold in packages and how many are in the package.
    Distribute copies of Master 44. Direct children's attention to the page. Have children identify the objects pictured. Tell them to count the number of objects in each package and to ring the

packages that have twelve items inside. Have children complete the page independently. Call on volunteers to explain their answers.

Extension
Give 12 counters to each child. Ask children to arrange 12 counters in equal rows. Have them compare groups and tell how many there are in each row. [Possible groups: 1 row of 12, 2 rows of 6, 3 rows of 4, 4 rows of 3, 6 rows of 2, 12 rows of 1]

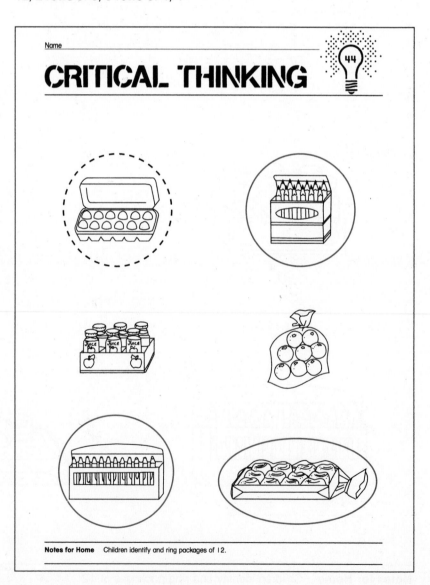

Name _____

CRITICAL THINKING

44

Notes for Home   Children identify and ring packages of 12.

45

PROBLEM SOLVING

| 11 | 11 | 12 | 12 | 11 | 11 | _12_ |

| 12 | 11 | 12 | 11 | 12 | _ _ _ _ |

| 11 | 12 | 11 | 12 | 11 | _ _ _ _ |

| 10 | 11 | 12 | 10 | 11 | _ _ _ _ |

_ _ _ _ _ _ _ _ _ _ _ _ _ _ _ _ _ _

_ _ _ _ _ _ _ _ _ _ _ _ _ _ _ _ _ _

Notes for Home Children write what comes next in a pattern. Then they write their own patterns.

Use with
Objective 45
   pages 127–128

Focus
Problem Solving
   Find a Pattern

Overview
This problem-solving activity will provide children with an opportunity to analyze and think logically. Children identify and complete patterns with numerals.

Materials
• chalk

Teaching Suggestions
Write rows of 11 and 12 on the chalkboard. Call on volunteers, in turn, to trace over a number using a piece of colored chalk. Give each child an opportunity to trace a number.

   Distribute copies of Master 45. Direct children's attention to the page. Discuss the pattern at the top of the page. Explain why the numbers make a pattern. [They are repeated.] Have children look at the number patterns on the page and write the number that comes next. Children then can make their own number pattern with the numbers 11 and 12. Check children's answers.

Extension
Write the numbers 11 and 12 on drawing paper, one number on each sheet. Use large numerals. Give each child a paper. Have

children first trace over the number with a crayon and then decorate the number or make a picture from it.

Encourage children to use their imaginations. Place the pictures on a bulletin-board display when completed.

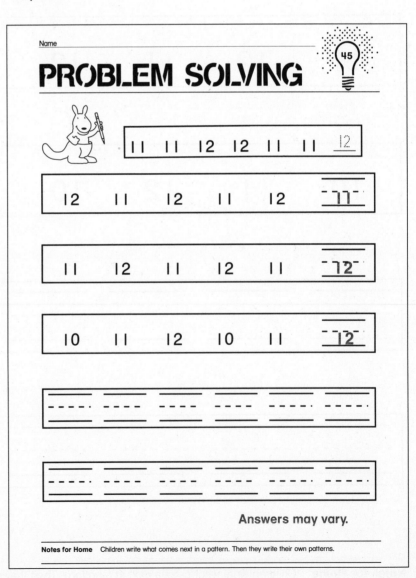

Name _____

PROBLEM SOLVING

45

| 11 | 11 | 12 | 12 | 11 | 11 | 12 |

| 12 | 11 | 12 | 11 | 12 | 11 |

| 11 | 12 | 11 | 12 | 11 | 12 |

| 10 | 11 | 12 | 10 | 11 | 12 |

| - |

| - |

Answers may vary.

Notes for Home   Children write what comes next in a pattern. Then they write their own patterns.

VISUAL THINKING

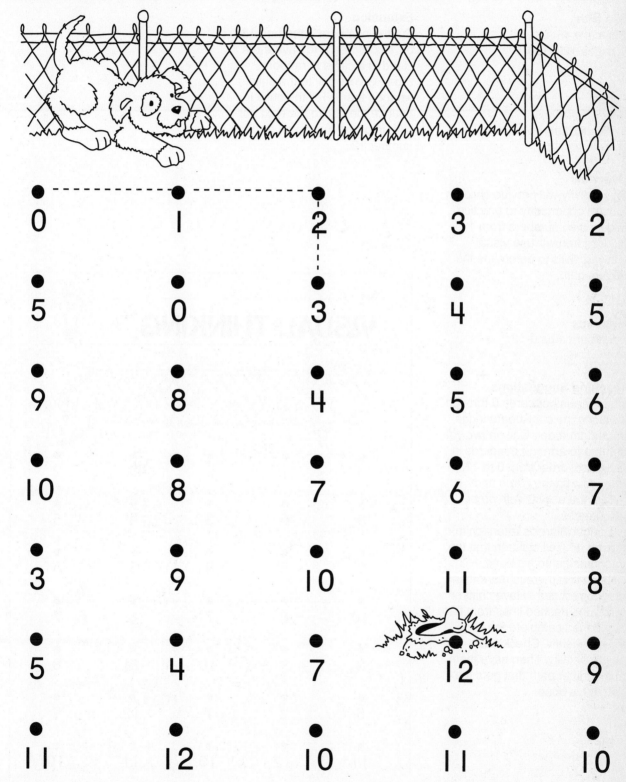

0	1	2	3	2
5	0	3	4	5
9	8	4	5	6
10	8	7	6	7
3	9	10	11	8
5	4	7	12	9
11	12	10	11	10

Notes for Home   Children order numbers 0 through 12 by connecting the dots.

Teacher Notes

Use with

Objective 46
   pages 129–130

Focus

Visual Thinking
   Visual Patterns

Overview

This activity will provide children with an opportunity to practice sequencing numbers from 1 to 12. Children will use visual-thinking skills to determine the correct path.

Materials

• number cards 0-12

Teaching Suggestions

Display number cards 0 through 12 along the chalkboard ledge in random order. Call on two volunteers to arrange the cards in numerical order from 0 to 12. Then mix up the cards and repeat the activity with other volunteers.

   Direct children's attention to Master 46. Tell children that the dog must get to his bone. Explain that there is more than one correct path. Have children follow the dashed lines from 0 to 3 and then complete the page independently. Check each child's activity. Then have them find another path that gets the dog to his bone.

Extension

Put the numbers 0 through 12 on 13 children and have them stand in a circle in random order. Give a ball to the child wearing the 0. Tell the child to bounce the ball to the next person, in order, and so on through number 12.

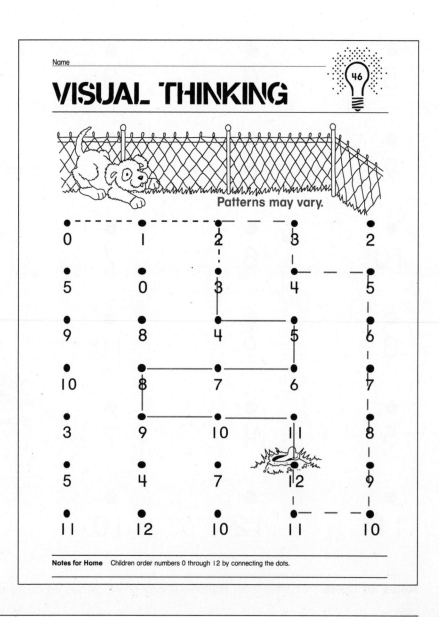

DECISION MAKING

Notes for Home   Children compare numbers by drawing a line from the child to their building.

Teacher Notes

Use with
Objective 47
  pages 131–132

Focus
Decision Making

Overview
This activity will provide children with an opportunity to analyze a problem and make a decision. Children decide where each child lives by counting windows.

Materials
• 10 laces
• 10 beads

Teaching Suggestions
Display 6 laces and 8 beads on a table. **Question:** *Which group has more objects?* [beads] Then ask eight children to stand near the table. **Questions:** *Can each child be given one lace?* [No] *Can each child choose one bead?* [Yes] *Are there more or fewer laces than children?* [fewer laces] *Are there fewer beads than children?* [No] Repeat with other amounts of laces and beads.

Direct children's attention to Master 47. Explain to the children that some people live in apartment buildings. Discuss the differences between apartment buildings and family houses. Then have children draw a line and match each child to the correct building. Ask children to identify the clues in the picture that will help them

make a match. [Numbers on each child's shirt, number of windows] Check children's answers.

Extension
Assign children to work in groups of three. Ask each child to pick less than 12 counters. Have children in each group compare the number of counters they picked. Ask them to arrange the three sets in order, with the least number at the top of the group and the largest number at the bottom. If two children picked up the same number of counters, they should arrange the two sets side by side. Compare the smallest and the largest groups. Ask what is the difference between the groups.

Name

DECISION MAKING
47

CRITICAL THINKING

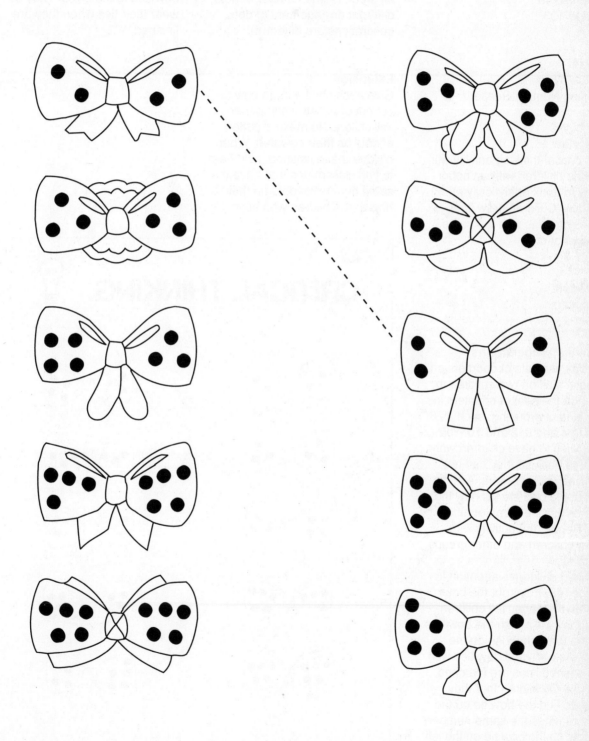

Notes for Home   Children match the bow tie on the left with the one on the right to make a pair.

Use with
Objective 48
  page 133

Focus
Critical Thinking
  Using Number Sense

Overview
This critical-thinking activity will provide children with an opportunity to think analytically and logically. Children draw lines to match pictures with the same number of dots.

Materials
• counters

Teaching Suggestions
Display two sets of counters on a table. Call on two children to arrange their set of counters in any kind of grouping, such as 6 and 6, 4 and 8, 2 and 10. You may wish to have children work back to back so they can not see each other's work. Ask the rest of the class to tell how the groups are the same or different. Repeat the activity with other children and other groups up to 12.

Direct children's attention to Master 48. Point out the bow ties on the page. Tell children that they will match the bow ties on the left with those on the right. Ask why the bow ties with the dashed lines are matched. Explain to children that they have to find the bow tie on the right that has the same number of dots as the bow tie on the left.

When children have finished the page, discuss how the pairs of bow ties are the same and different. (same number of dots; different arrangement of dots; decorations are different)

Extension
Give each child a large bow tie cut out of construction paper. Tell children to make a pattern of dots on their bow ties. When children have finished, ask them to find classmates that have the same number of dots on their bow ties. Children who have found a match should show their bow ties to the class. They can wear their ties when they are finished.

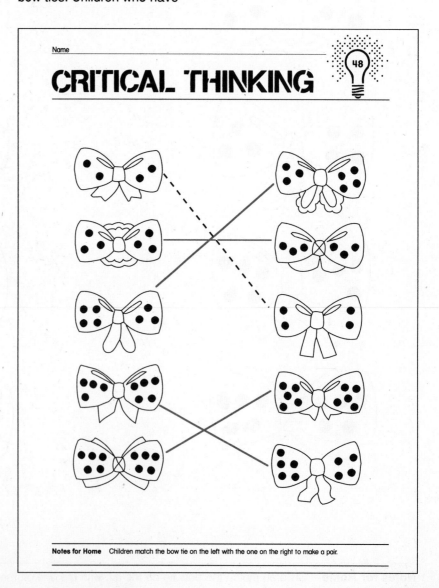

Name _____

CRITICAL THINKING

48

Notes for Home   Children match the bow tie on the left with the one on the right to make a pair.

CRITICAL THINKING

Notes for Home   Children color the picture that shows what happens last in each row.

Use after pages 141–142.

Use with

Objective 49
pages 141–142

Focus

Critical Thinking
Drawing Conclusions

Overview

This activity will provide children with an opportunity to think analytically and logically. Children study pictures and decide which will probably happen last.

Teaching Suggestions

Call on a volunteer to follow your directions. Whisper to the child to pick up a piece of chalk, write his or her name on the chalkboard, and then put the chalk on the chalkboard ledge. Have the child follow your directions in sequential order. Then ask children to tell what the child did first; last. Repeat with other children and different directions.

Distribute copies of Master 49. Direct children's attention to row 1. Have children describe what is happening in the first two pictures. Then have them color the picture on the right-hand side that shows what probably happened last. Repeat this procedure for row 2. Have children explain their answers.

Extension

Ask children to bring in three pictures of themselves taken at three different ages, from birth to the present. Display each child's pictures in order on a bulletin board. Then discuss how they have changed during these years. Have them predict how they will change in the next year.

Name _____

CRITICAL THINKING

color

color

Notes for Home   Children color the picture that shows what happens last in each row.

VISUAL THINKING

Notes for Home Children find the path that takes less time by drawing a line to the house. Then they mark an X on the path that takes more time.

Use with

Objective 50
    pages 143–144

Focus

Visual Thinking
    Spatial Perception

Overview

This activity will provide children with an opportunity to use visual-thinking skills and make judgments. Children will trace two mazes visually and decide which one took less time to do.

Teaching Suggestions

Call on two volunteers to go on walks in the classroom. Have one child walk the length of the room and stop. At the same time, have the second child walk from the door to a nearby desk or table. Ask children to name the child who took the longer walk. Continue the activity with other volunteers and different locations in the room.

   Distribute copies of Master 50. Direct children's attention to the page. Explain that the two squirrels are each taking a path to Grandmother's house. Ask children who they think will get to Grandmother's house first and to explain why. [The male squirrel will get there first because his path is shorter.] Have children trace both paths with their finger. Tell children to draw a line down the path that takes less time to complete. Then they can put an X on the path that takes more time.

Extension

Have children pantomime washing their hands. Then ask children to listen as you list other activities. Tell them to stand up if the activity takes a longer time than washing hands, or they are to sit down if the activity takes a shorter time than washing hands. List activities such as the ones below.

taking a bath
blinking
watching a movie

eating dinner
walking (or riding) to school
swallowing
coughing
sleeping at night

Name _____

VISUAL THINKING

Notes for Home   Children find the path that takes less time by drawing a line to the house. Then they mark an X on the path that takes more time.

VISUAL THINKING

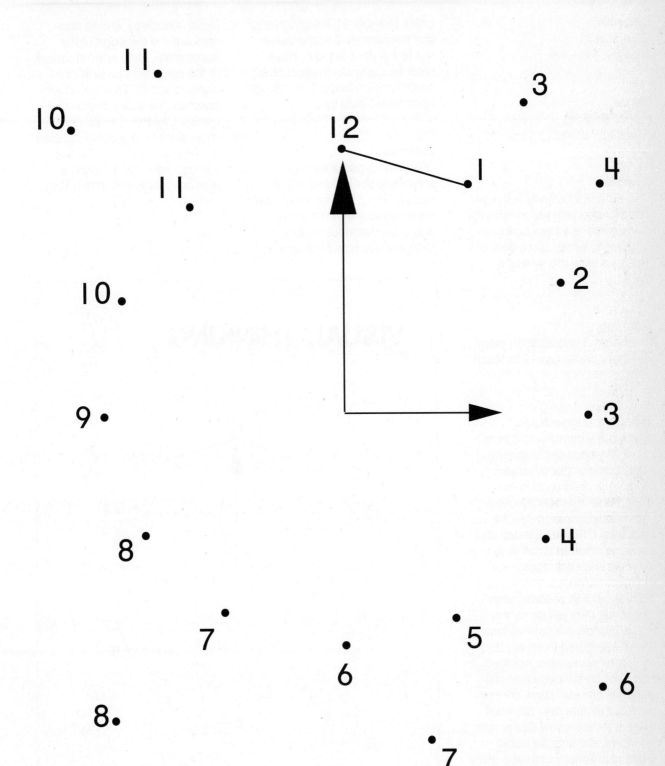

Notes for Home   Children connect the dots to make the face of a traditional clock.

Problem Solving and Critical Thinking/**EXPLORING MATHEMATICS** © Scott, Foresman and Company/**K**   Use after pages 145 –146.

51

Teacher Notes

Use with
Objective 51
    pages 145–146

Focus
Visual Thinking
    Visual Patterns

Overview
This dot-to-dot activity will provide children with an opportunity to visualize and form a picture. Children choose from a field of dots to outline the face of a clock.

Materials
• standard demonstration clock
• number cards 1 to 12 for each child

Teaching Suggestions
Distribute a number card from 1 to 12 to each child. Show 9 o'clock on the demonstration clock. Ask children to hold up the number that tells the time. Then ask children to say the time aloud. Repeat the activity, showing different times in random order on the clock.

Direct children's attention to Master 51. Ask children what they think they will do on this page. [Follow the dots according to the numbers.] Point out that there are some extra numbers and dots on the page that children will not use. Have children tell what picture they think will appear if they follow all the right numbers and dots. [a clock]

Have children put their pencils on the dot under the number 1. Ask them to identify the number that comes next in sequential order. [number 2] Tell children to find the number 2 and draw a line to the dot next to it. Have children complete the rest of the page independently. Then check each child's activity.

Extension
Distribute paper plates and crayons to the children. Give each child a paper fastener and paper cutouts of a big hand and a little hand for a clock. Demonstrate how children can make a clock by writing numbers around the edge of the paper plate. Help children attach to the clock the hands with a paper fastener. They can then decorate the faces of their clocks. Children can ask each other what time a certain activity would occur. (Show what time you eat breakfast.) Continue with more activities of this kind.

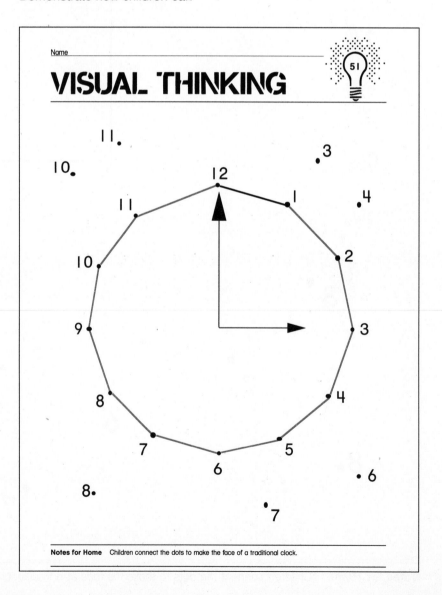

DECISION MAKING

Notes for Home   Children decide if the event takes place during the day or night. Then they ring the correct symbol.

Use with
Objective 52
pages 147–148

Focus
Decision Making

Overview
This activity will provide children with an opportunity to analyze a situation and the options before making a decision. Children study pictures and decide whether events should take place during the day or at night.

Materials
• demonstration clock

Teaching Suggestions
Show 7 o'clock on the demonstration clock. Explain that the clock shows a time when many people wake up in the morning. Ask them what time it is. Discuss with children the kinds of activities people do when they get up. Then show 9:00 on the clock. Point out that this is the time of morning that most people are in school or at work. Ask them what time it is. Continue the activity with these times: 12:00 [noon, lunchtime]; 5:00 [in the late afternoon, most working people are starting home]; 9:00 [at night, most children are in bed or going to bed].

Direct children's attention to Master 52. Discuss the page by having children identify the four activities. Tell children to ring the sun under each picture if it shows something that happens during the day, or to ring the

moon under each picture if it shows something that happens at night. Call on volunteers to explain their answers.

Extension
Call on children to pantomime activities that they do during the day (from morning to bedtime). Have the other children guess the activity and tell when the activity probably takes place. (morning, afternoon, nighttime) Children should also be encouraged to predict the possible time each activity takes place.

Name _____

DECISION MAKING

52

Notes for Home Children decide if the event takes place during the day or night. Then they ring the correct symbol.

CRITICAL THINKING

Notes for Home   Children identify first through fifth positions by drawing a line from the frog to the lily pad according to oral directions.

Teacher Notes

Use with
Objective 53
    pages 149–150

Focus
Critical Thinking
    Finding, Extending,
    and Using Patterns

Overview
This activity will provide children with an opportunity to think analytically and logically. Children identify ordinal patterns of frogs and lily pads.

Teaching Suggestions
Line up five volunteers in front of the classroom. Have them face left. Have the class name the child whose position you identify. **Questions:** *Who is first in line? Who is third in line? Who is second in line? Is (child's name) the fourth or fifth person in line?*

Distribute copies of Master 53. Direct children's attention to the page. Have the pictures identified. [frogs and lily pads] Tell children that you are going to give them some directions about the frogs and how they jump to the lily pads. Have children listen to each direction, find the correct frog, and draw a line to the correct lily pad. Give the following directions:
  • The first frog jumped to the second lily pad.
  • The third frog jumped to the first lily pad.
  • The fourth frog jumped to the fifth lily pad.
  • The second frog jumped to the third lily pad.

  • The fifth frog jumped to the fourth lily pad.
    Have children show their work and explain their answers. (Note: There is an extra lily pad to help ensure that children do not just automatically think the last lily pad is the *fifth* lily pad)

Extension
Divide sheets of drawing paper into 5 equal parts. Distribute crayons and drawing paper to the children. Identify the five boxes on the paper as first to fifth. Using ordinals in random order, give children directions to draw simple objects in each box; for example, "Draw an apple in the third box. Draw a hat in the fifth box. Draw a happy face in the first box. Draw a ball in the second box. Draw a flower in the fourth box." Check each child's picture.

Name _____

CRITICAL THINKING

Notes for Home   Children identify first through fifth positions by drawing a line from the frog to the lily pad according to oral directions.

CRITICAL THINKING

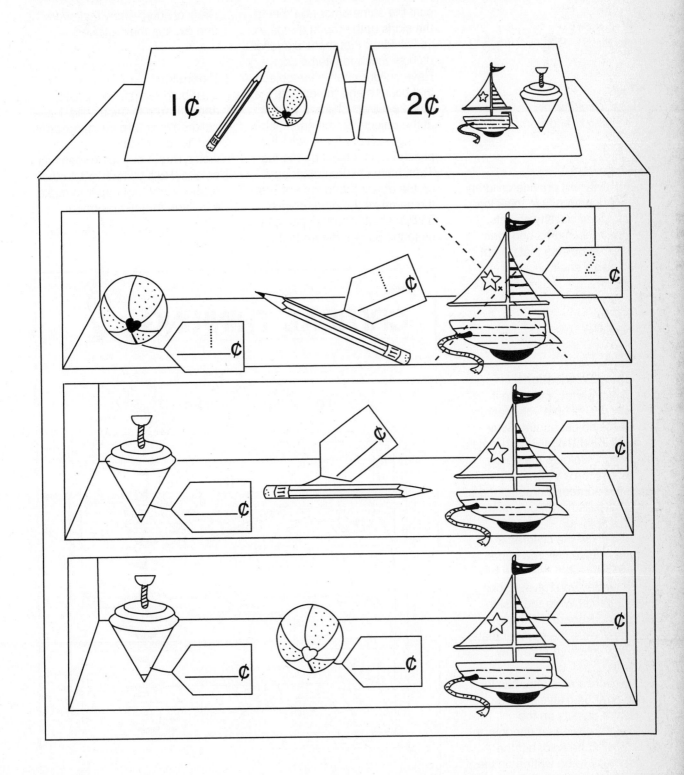

Notes for Home Children determine the price of each object. Then they mark an X on the object that does not belong on each shelf.

Problem Solving and Critical Thinking/**EXPLORING MATHEMATICS** © Scott, Foresman and Company/K

Use after pages 151–152.

Teacher Notes

Use with

Objective 54
  pages 151–152

Focus

Critical Thinking
  Classifying and Sorting

Overview

This activity will provide children with an opportunity to think logically as they classify objects. Children price items and then identify the objects that do not belong on a shelf.

Materials

• 2 pennies

Teaching Suggestions

Hold up a penny and have it identified. Call on a volunteer to name the object another way. [1 cent] On the chalkboard write the ¢ sign. Hold up the penny again. Call on a volunteer to write the number in front of the ¢ sign that tells how much money you are holding.

Then show the children 2 pennies. Have children name the two ways that describe how much money you have. [2 pennies, 2 cents] Write the ¢ sign on the chalkboard and have a volunteer write the number that tells how much you are now holding.

Direct children's attention to the Master 54. Have children name the objects on the shelves. Explain that the objects are going to be sold, but the prices need to be written on the tags. Point out that all the objects on each shelf

should cost the same amount. Point to the signs at the top of the page. Tell children that these signs tell us how much the items cost. Have children name the objects that cost 1¢ and the objects that cost 2¢. Direct children to look at the objects on the shelf below the signs. Have them write the price of each object on the tag. Then have children mark an X on the object that does not cost the same as the other objects on that shelf. Children can complete the page independently.

Have children show their work and explain their answers.

Extension

Distribute magazines, paste, and scissors to each child. Have children look through magazines and cut out pictures that they would like to buy for 10 pennies or less. Help children paste their pictures on chart paper to make a collage for the classroom.

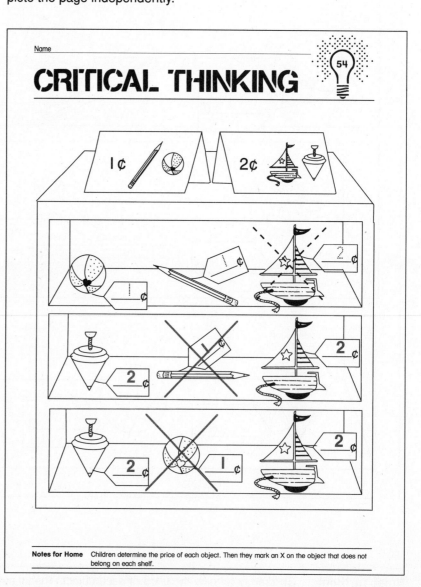

Name _____

CRITICAL THINKING

54

1¢   2¢

Notes for Home Children determine the price of each object. Then they mark an X on the object that does not belong on each shelf.

VISUAL THINKING

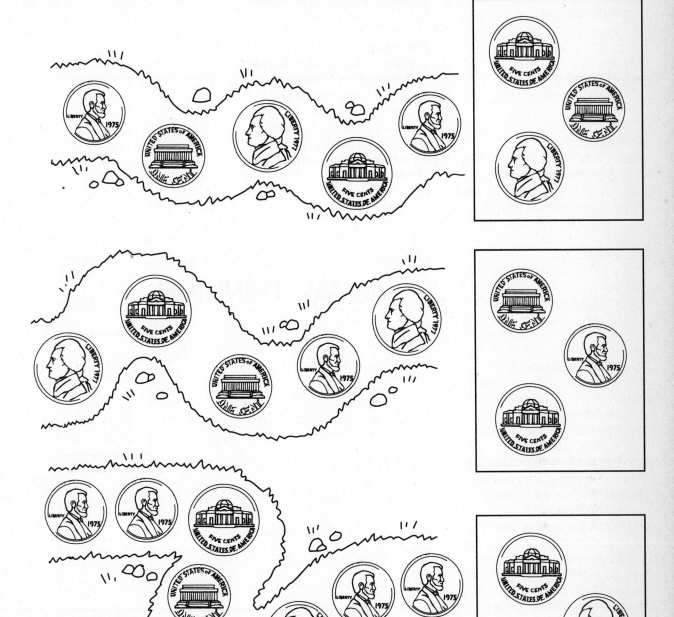

Notes for Home Children identify patterns with two-sided pennies and nickels. They determine the next coin in each pattern.

Problem Solving and Critical Thinking/**EXPLORING MATHEMATICS** © Scott, Foresman and Company/**K**   Use after pages 153–154.

Teacher Notes

Use with
Objective 55
   pages 153–154

Focus
Visual Thinking
   Visual Patterns

Overview
This activity will provide children with an opportunity to make judgments. Children identify patterns of pennies and nickels.

Materials
• 2 punchout nickels for each child
• 5 punchout pennies for each child

Teaching Suggestions
Distribute 2 nickels and 5 pennies to each child. Have children put the money in a pile. Then ask them to take out 1 nickel and 1 penny and hold up a coin in each hand. Have children tell how much money they are holding. [6¢] Repeat with other groups of coins.

   Distribute copies of Master 55. Direct children's attention to the page. Point out that each group of coins is arranged in a pattern. Discuss the pattern in the first row. You may wish to make sure children are familiar with the appearance of heads and tails on each coin. Have children color in the coin in the box at the right to show what coin would be next in the pattern. Ask a volunteer to explain the answer. Have children complete the rest of the page independently. Call on volunteers to show and explain their answers.

Extension
Distribute 10 punchout nickels and 10 punchout pennies to each pair of children. Have children use the coins to make their own patterns. Each child may make a pattern of coins for a friend to guess. Check children's work.

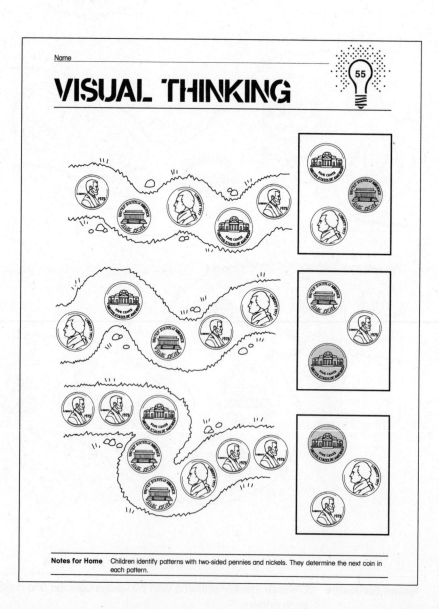

Name _____

VISUAL THINKING

55

Notes for Home Children identify patterns with two-sided pennies and nickels. They determine the next coin in each pattern.

CRITICAL THINKING

54

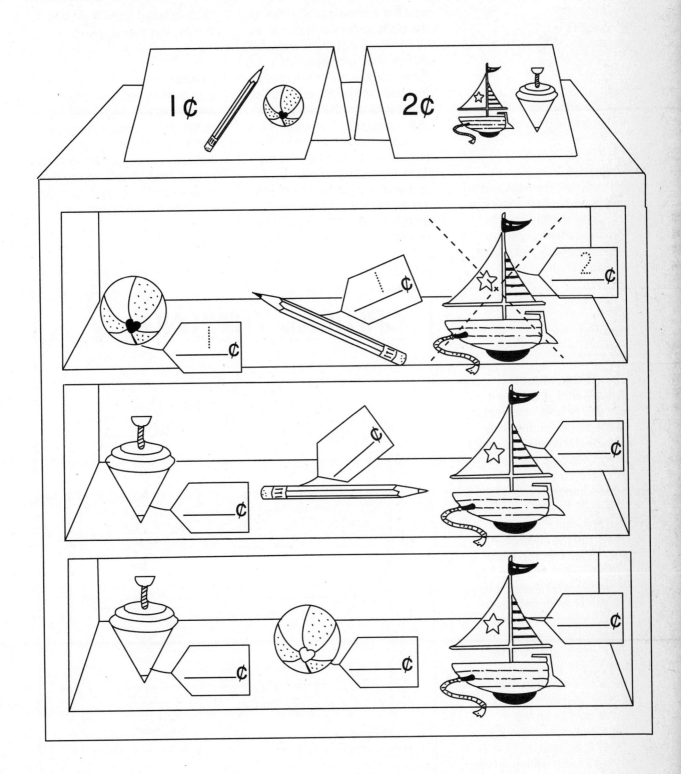

Notes for Home Children determine the price of each object. Then they mark an X on the object that does not belong on each shelf.

Use after pages 151–152.

Use with

Objective 54
   pages 151–152

Focus

Critical Thinking
   Classifying and Sorting

Overview

This activity will provide children with an opportunity to think logically as they classify objects. Children price items and then identify the objects that do not belong on a shelf.

Materials

• 2 pennies

Teaching Suggestions

Hold up a penny and have it identified. Call on a volunteer to name the object another way. [1 cent] On the chalkboard write the ¢ sign. Hold up the penny again. Call on a volunteer to write the number in front of the ¢ sign that tells how much money you are holding.

   Then show the children 2 pennies. Have children name the two ways that describe how much money you have. [2 pennies, 2 cents] Write the ¢ sign on the chalkboard and have a volunteer write the number that tells how much you are now holding.

   Direct children's attention to the Master 54. Have children name the objects on the shelves. Explain that the objects are going to be sold, but the prices need to be written on the tags. Point out that all the objects on each shelf should

cost the same amount. Point to the signs at the top of the page. Tell children that these signs tell us how much the items cost. Have children name the objects that cost 1¢ and the objects that cost 2¢. Direct children to look at the objects on the shelf below the signs. Have them write the price of each object on the tag. Then have children mark an X on the object that does not cost the same as the other objects on that shelf. Children can complete the page independently.

Have children show their work and explain their answers.

Extension

Distribute magazines, paste, and scissors to each child. Have children look through magazines and cut out pictures that they would like to buy for 10 pennies or less. Help children paste their pictures on chart paper to make a collage for the classroom.

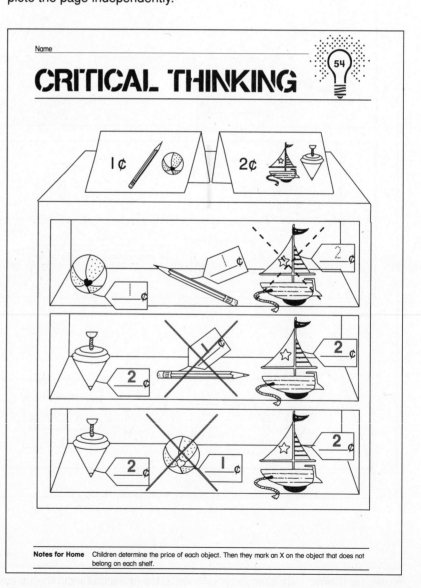

Name _____

CRITICAL THINKING

54

1¢   2¢

Notes for Home   Children determine the price of each object. Then they mark an X on the object that does not belong on each shelf.

VISUAL THINKING

Notes for Home   Children color the dimes blue and the pennies brown to discover the hidden picture.

Use with
Objective 56
pages 155–156

Focus
Visual Thinking
Spatial Perception

Overview
This activity will provide children with an opportunity to analyze information from pictures. Children color certain coins to discover a hidden picture.

Materials
• 15 punchout pennies
• 3 punchout nickels
• 1 punchout dime

Teaching Suggestions
Hold up a punchout dime. Ask children what you are holding and how much it is worth. [a dime; worth 10 cents] Then place the dime on a table. Place the 15 punchout pennies and 3 nickels near the dime. Call on a volunteer to pick out the nickels that are worth the same as the dime. Call on another volunteer to do the same activity with the pennies.

Distribute copies of Master 56. Direct children's attention to the page. Explain that there is a picture hidden among the coins. Tell children that they will be coloring only the dimes and pennies on the page. Have them color each dime blue and each penny brown. Call on volunteers to show their completed pictures and tell what they see. [a girl blowing bubbles with a bubble pipe]

Extension
Distribute drawing paper, crayons, paste, and precut silver or white circles to the children. Have them draw something that they would like to buy for 10 cents. Then have children paste the silver circle onto their papers to represent 1 dime or 10 cents. Call on volunteers to show and tell about their drawings.

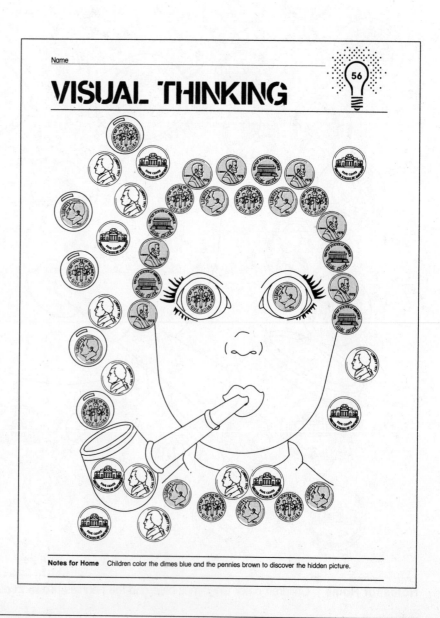

Name _____

VISUAL THINKING

Notes for Home   Children color the dimes blue and the pennies brown to discover the hidden picture.

PROBLEM SOLVING

57

| 8¢ |  |  |  |  |  |

| 11¢ |  | | | | |

| 10¢ | | | | | |

| 12¢ |  | | | |  |

Notes for Home Children make a graph by marking an X on the correct coins for each amount.

Teacher Notes

Use with
Objective 57
   pages 157–158

Focus
Problem Solving
   Make a Graph

Overview
This activity will provide children with an opportunity to use information in making a graph. Children mark an X on each coin to show the money value.

Materials
• 10 brown paper badges
• 2 gray paper badges
• 1 silver paper badge
• safety pins

Teaching Suggestions
Pin the badges on 13 volunteers. Have children stand in the front of the room in groups according to the color of their badges. Explain that the brown badges are the pennies, the gray badges are the nickels, and the silver badge is the dime. *Questions: How much is the brown badge group worth?* [10¢] *How much are the gray badges worth together?* [10¢] *How much is the silver badge worth?* [10¢] *How can we make another group that is worth 10¢?* (Put a child with a gray badge in a group with 5 children with brown badges.) If children do not suggest this way of grouping, regroup the children to see that this group is worth the same as the others in money value.
   Distribute copies of Master 57. Direct children's attention to the page. Have them point to 8¢ in the first row. Have the coins identified in the row. [nickel, penny, penny, penny, penny]

Then have children read aloud the money amounts in the other rows. Tell children to mark an X on the correct coins in each row to show the amount. Have children complete the page independently. Call on volunteers to explain their answers.

Extension
Make and distribute paper badges for the rest of the class. Provide approximately equal numbers of brown badges (pennies), gray badges (nickels), and silver badges (dimes). On index cards write money amounts from 1¢ to 12¢. Pin the badges on the children. Review the coins each color badge represents. Call on a volunteer to select an index card and read the amount. Then have that child call on as many children as needed to equal the amount. Repeat this activity with another volunteer.

Name _____

PROBLEM SOLVING

57

8¢

11¢

10¢

12¢

Pennies may vary.

VISUAL THINKING

58

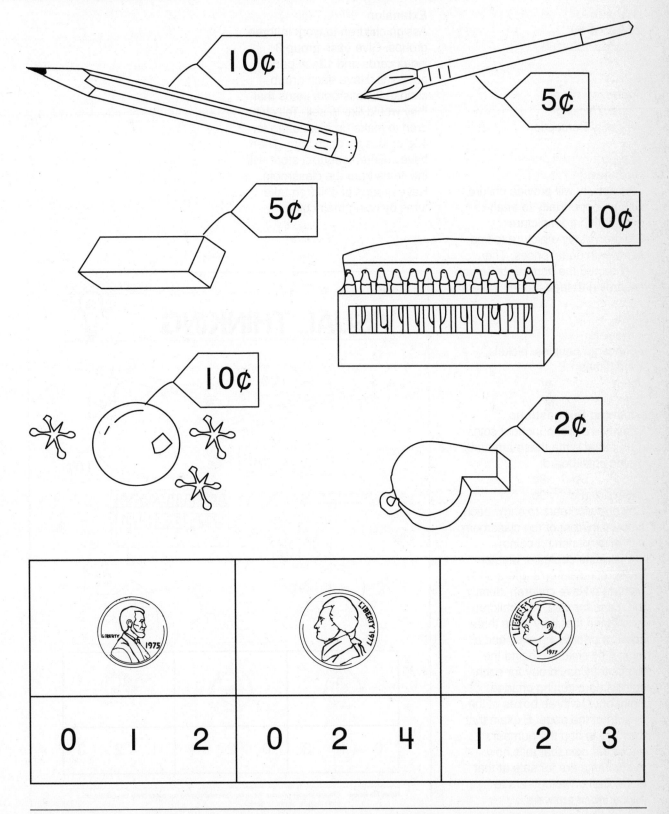

Notes for Home   Children identify prices at the store. Then they ring the number of items for sale that either costs pennies, nickels, or dimes.

Problem Solving and Critical Thinking/**EXPLORING MATHEMATICS** © Scott, Foresman and Company/K   Use after pages 159–160.

Use with
Objective 58
pages 159–160

Focus
Visual Thinking
Spatial Perception

Overview
This activity will provide children with an opportunity to analyze information from pictures. Children study a picture to find items with equal prices. Then they record the number of items according to their money value.

Materials
• punchout pennies, nickels, and dimes

Teaching Suggestions
Display a set of punchout coins on a table. Write these amounts on the chalkboard:

5¢	6¢	8¢
12¢	10¢	9¢

Call on volunteers to show each amount in front of the classroom using the punchout coins.

Distribute copies of Master 58. Direct children's attention to the page. Have children identify the items for sale. Ask children to imagine that they have three coins: a penny, a nickel, and a dime. Tell children to find the things they could buy for each coin without getting change. Point out the three boxes at the bottom of the page. Explain that they are to ring the number under the coin that tells how many items are for sale at that price. Call on volunteers to explain their answers.

Extension
Assign children to work in three groups. Give each group 3 index cards and 12¢ in punch-out coins. Have each group choose 3 classroom items that they would like to sell. Tell children to make up a price tag for 12¢ or less for each item. Then have children set up a store with the items from the classroom. Have groups of children take turns by using their coins.

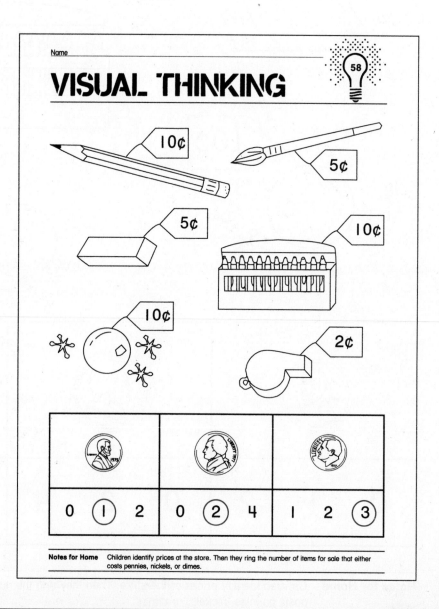

DECISION MAKING

59

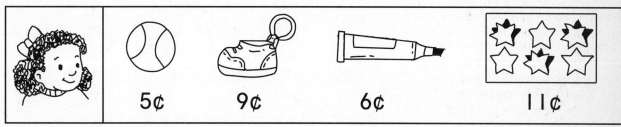

5¢   9¢   6¢   11¢

5¢   10¢   12¢   8¢

Notes for Home   Children count the value of the coins. Then they ring the items each child can purchase and mark an X on the items they can not purchase.

Use with
Objective 59
   page 161

Focus
Decision Making

Overview
This activity will provide children with an opportunity to analyze a problem and identify information needed for making a decision. Children determine the value of the pictured coins. Then they find items that can be purchased with those given amounts.

Materials
• 5 pennies
• 1 nickel
• a ball
• an eraser

Teaching Suggestions
Ask for two volunteers. Give one child a nickel and a penny. Give the other child four pennies. Then show the children a ball. *Question: Who can pay me 6¢ for this ball?* Have children decide which of them can buy the ball. Have that child pantomime the purchase. Repeat the activity with two other volunteers and two different amounts of money. Give one child 3 pennies and the other child 4 pennies. Price the eraser at 4¢ and have children decide who can buy the eraser.

   Distribute copies of Master 59. Direct children's attention to the page. Tell children that the children on the page are counting their coins. Point out that the same children are shown in the boxes at the bottom of the page. Have children ring every item each child can buy with the

amount of coins they have. Then they cross out any item they can't buy. Have children complete the page independently. Check each child's activity.

Extension
On index cards, write amounts from 1¢ through 12¢. Put the cards in a deck in random order. Divide the class into two teams and have each team decide on a captain. Call on one member of each team to draw an index card from the deck. Have these

children show the cards to both teams to decide which of the two amounts is greater. When the team is ready, the captain should raise a hand. Call on the first captain that raises a hand. Give one point for each correct answer. Keep a tally on the chalkboard. Make sure all members of each team have turns. Then have children count the tally marks to determine the winning team.

VISUAL THINKING

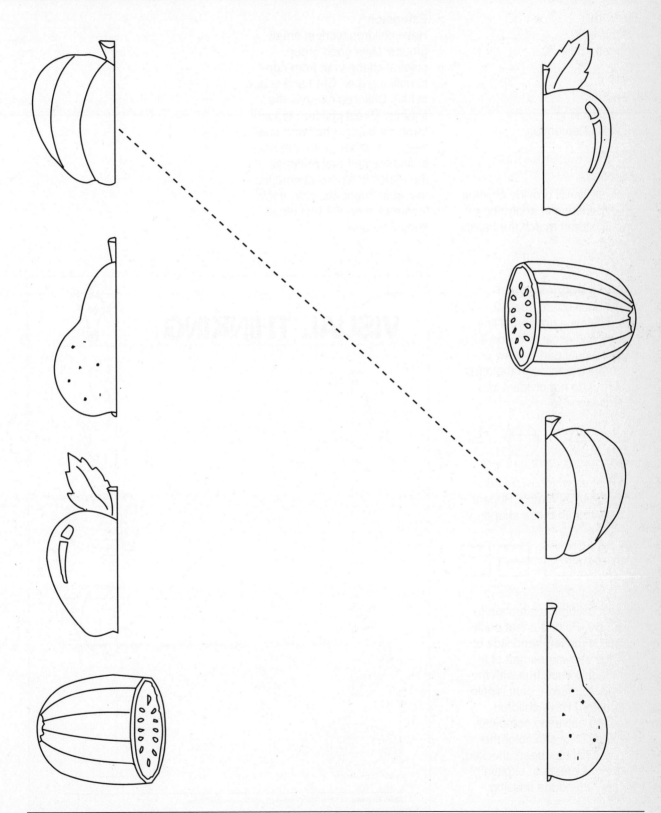

Notes for Home   Children identify halves by matching two parts of fruit.

Problem Solving and Critical Thinking/**EXPLORING MATHEMATICS** © Scott, Foresman and Company/K   Use after pages 169–170.

Use with

Objective 60
  pages 169–170

Focus

Visual Thinking
  Spatial Perception

Overview

This activity will provide children with experience in analyzing pictures. Children match the halves of fruits.

Teaching Suggestions

On the chalkboard, draw 2 circles. Draw a horizontal line through one circle to divide it into two equal parts. Draw a horizontal line through the other circle, but do not divide it into two equal parts.

Ask children which circle has two halves that match. Repeat the activity with these shapes.

  Direct children's attention to Master 60. Point out that each picture on the left-hand side of the page shows one half of a fruit. Identify each fruit with the children. [pumpkin, pear, apple, watermelon] Have children match the halves to complete the page. They can color the page when it has been checked. Call on volunteers to explain how they found the missing halves.

Extension

Have children work in small groups. Give each group several shapes cut from construction paper. Cut each shape in half. Children can mix the shapes. Direct children to take turns choosing a half and challenging another group member to find the half that matches. If the match is a correct one, then the latter keeps the pair. If it is incorrect, then the first player keeps the pair.

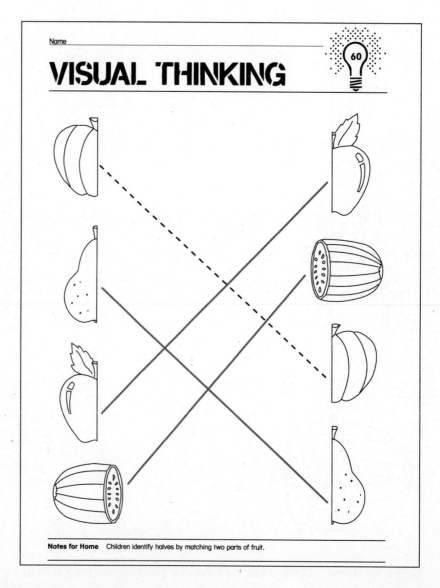

PROBLEM SOLVING

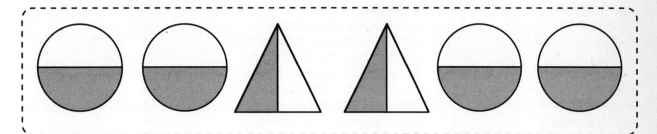

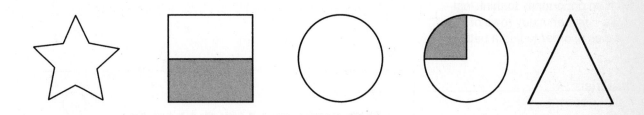

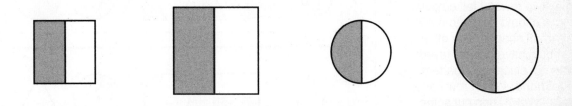

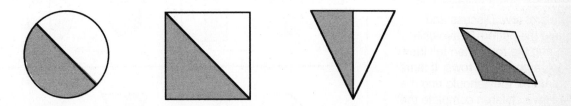

Notes for Home   Children identify and ring the rows that show a pattern of shapes.

Problem Solving and Critical Thinking/**EXPLORING MATHEMATICS** © Scott, Foresman and Company/**K**   Use after pages 171–172.

Teacher Notes

Use with
Objective 61
   pages 171–172

Focus
Problem Solving
   Find a Pattern

Overview
This activity will provide children with an opportunity to think logically. Children study rows of shapes in order to find a pattern.

Materials
- flannel board
- felt shapes and objects
- paper objects

Teaching Suggestions
Display two rows of felt cutouts. One row should be layed out in a pattern of shapes. The other row should have objects layed out but not placed in a pattern.
   Questions: Which row has a pattern? Why? Then cut some paper objects in half. Call on volunteers to make patterns with these cutouts.
   Direct children's attention to Master 61. Have children look at the first row. Discuss and explain the pattern. Have children ring the row. Then tell them to look at the other rows. If there is a pattern, they should ring the row. Have children complete the page independently. Call on volunteers to explain their answers.

Extension
Give magazines, scissors, paste, and drawing paper to the children. Have them cut out two pictures of objects from a magazine. Tell the children to cut the pictures in half. They can exchange the picture halves with a classmate. Then children can paste their halves together to make a whole object.

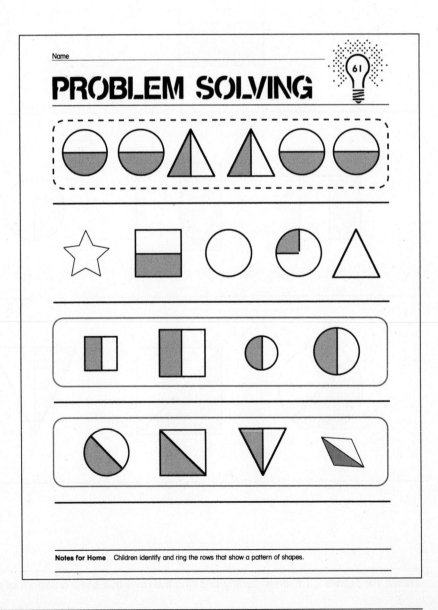

Name _____

PROBLEM SOLVING

Notes for Home   Children identify and ring the rows that show a pattern of shapes.

VISUAL THINKING

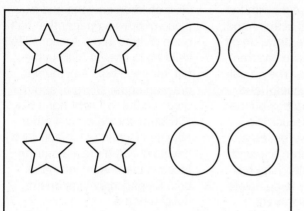

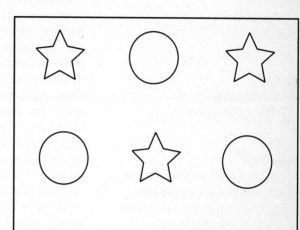

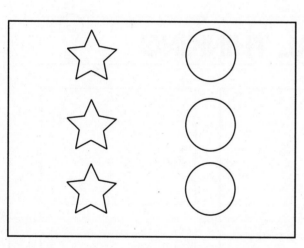

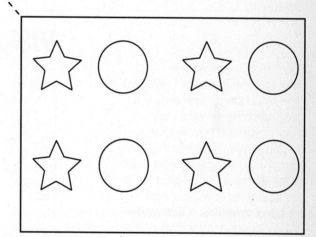

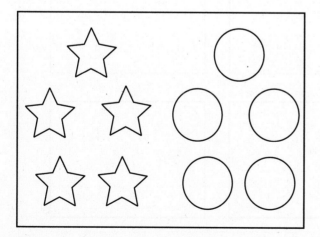

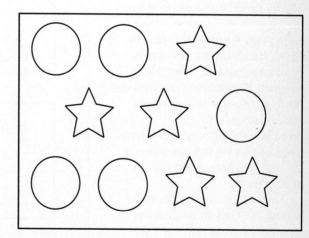

Notes for Home   Children identify and match sets of equal shares of objects.

Teacher Notes

Use with
Objective 62
  pages 173–174

Focus
Visual Thinking
  Spatial Perception

Overview
This activity will provide children with the opportunity to make judgments. Children match sets of equal shares of objects.

Materials
• 8 pennies

Teaching Suggestions
Display the 8 pennies. Have two volunteers stand near the pennies. Ask children how they might share the pennies between the two volunteers. (Children should suggest giving them equal shares.) Give 5 pennies to one volunteer and 2 pennies to the other volunteer. **Question: *Did I give equal shares to both children?* [No] *Who has more pennies?***

Now divide the pennies evenly. Have each volunteer demonstrate their 4 pennies. Ask children to tell if the volunteers have equal shares. [Yes] Have volunteers count their pennies aloud to prove that they have equal shares.

Repeat the activity with 6 pennies, first giving out unequal shares and then giving out equal shares.

Direct children's attention to Master 62. Call on a volunteer to describe what is in the top box at the left. [4 stars and 4

circles] Explain that there is another box at the right with the same equal shares of stars and circles, but they are drawn in different positions. Have children find the correct box. They must draw a line from the left-hand box to the matching box on the right-hand side. Discuss the sets in the other two boxes at the left. Have children find and draw lines to the matching box at the right in order to complete the page. Have volunteers explain their answers.

Extension
Give children crayons and a piece of drawing paper that has been divided into 4 sections. Tell children to draw 4 balls in the top left-hand box. Ask them to draw an equal share of another object in the top right-hand box. (Children should draw 4 other objects.) Continue the activity by having children draw 3 smiling faces in the bottom left-hand box. Display drawings on the bulletin board.

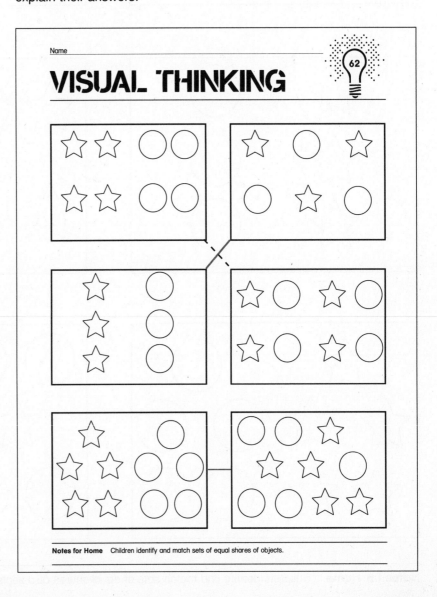

VISUAL THINKING

Notes for Home   Children identify and match sets of equal shares of objects.

DECISION MAKING

63

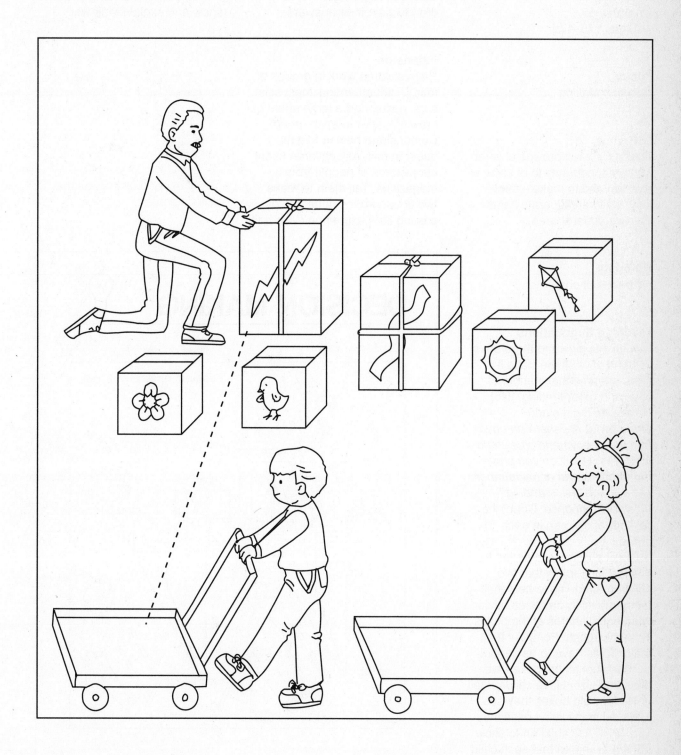

Notes for Home   Children draw a line to separate items into two equal shares.

Use with

Objective 63
    pages 175–176

Focus
Decision Making

Overview
This activity will provide children with an opportunity to analyze a problem and to make a decision. Children separate items into two equal shares.

Materials
• 4 pieces of chalk

Teaching Suggestions
Call on two girls and three boys to stand up. Ask the class if there are an equal number of boys and girls standing. [No] Have a third girl stand.
Questions: *Are there an equal number of boys and girls standing?* [Yes] *How can you prove that there are an equal number of boys and girls standing?* [Possible response: Count the number of children in each group.]
    Direct children's attention to Master 63. Explain that two children are going to help their father move some boxes by carrying equal shares of the boxes in their wagons. Point out that the children have to be careful because not all the boxes are the same size. Have children tell how many big boxes they see and how many little boxes they see. [2; 4] Ask children to show the equal shares that each child will carry by drawing a line from

each box to a wagon. Have children explain their answers.

Extension
Have children work in groups of four. Distribute magazines, scissors, paste, and a large sheet of drawing paper to each group. Demonstrate how to fold the paper in half. Ask children to cut out pictures of people from magazines. Tell them to make two equal groups of people by pasting the pictures on each half

of their paper. Call on groups to show and explain their work.

Name _____

DECISION MAKING

Possible answers shown.

Notes for Home   Children draw a line to separate items into two equal shares.

VISUAL THINKING

Notes for Home   Children find hidden pictures, make tally marks, and record how many.

Problem Solving and Critical Thinking/**EXPLORING MATHEMATICS** © Scott, Foresman and Company/**K**   Use after pages 177–178.

Teacher Notes

Use with
Objective 64
    pages 177–178

Focus
Visual Thinking
    Spatial Perception

Overview
This activity will provide children with an opportunity to analyze and get information from pictures. Children find hidden pictures, make tally marks, and record how many.

Teaching Suggestions
On the chalkboard draw 4 umbrellas. Have a volunteer make a tally mark for each umbrella and write the number that tells how many. [4] Repeat the activity by drawing 2 balls, 5 hearts, 6 apples, and 1 star.

Direct children's attention to Master 64. Ask children to tell what they see. Point out that there are hidden pictures of fish, balloons and moons. Review tally marks with children that are located below the picture. Have them look at the pictures near the bottom of the page and identify them. [fish, balloon, moon] Tell children they are to make a tally mark in the box for each fish, balloon, and moon they find in the big picture. Tell children they should then write the number that tells how many. Have children complete the page and color the hidden pictures independently. Call on volunteers to explain their answers.

Extension
Create a large tally chart for objects in the classroom. Set up the chart by drawing classroom objects on the left-hand side of the chart. Have volunteers tally the number of each pictured object. Here is a suggested chart.

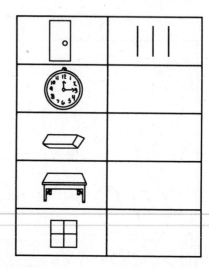

CRITICAL THINKING

_____

- - - - - - - - -

_____

- - - - - - - - -

_____

- - - - - - - - -

Notes for Home   Children ring the strongest person by counting the bars on each scale.

Teacher Notes

Use with
Objective 65
  pages 179–180

Focus
Critical Thinking
  Reasoning with Graphs and
  Charts

Overview
This activity will provide children
with an opportunity to think analytically and logically. Children
compare bars on a scale to find
the strongest person.

Materials
• 8 pennies

Teaching Suggestions
Display 3 pennies and have children count them aloud. Stack
the pennies. Then display 5
pennies and have them counted. Place these pennies in a
stack next to the other stack.
Ask children which stack is
higher. Repeat the activity with
stacks of 4 and 6 pennies, 2 and
3 pennies, 5 and 2 pennies.

Direct children's attention to
Master 65. Explain that the picture shows three men using
hammers trying to hit a target.
Discuss with children that this
contest is often held at carni-
vals. Tell them that the pole is
marked in bars. Have children
count the number of bars on
each pole. [5] Ask them if each
pole has the same number of
bars. [Yes] Have them count the
shaded bars of each weight and
then write the number on the
line below each picture. Tell children that they have to find and

ring the strongest man, the one
who has hit the target. Check
children's answers. Have them
explain their answers.

Extension
Have children work in various
size groups to make a pole of
one color. Cut out 1 pole for
each group from mural paper.
Paste a different colored paper
circle on each pole. Ask each
group to choose one of the
poles. Distribute large squares
of appropriate colors to each
group. Have children paste their
squares, one for each group
member, on their poles. When
the poles have been completed,
have children compare them
and count the squares. Poles
should reflect the amount of
members in each group.

Name _____

CRITICAL THINKING
65

— 4

— 3

— 5

Notes for Home   Children ring the strongest person by counting the bars on each scale.

CRITICAL THINKING

Notes for Home Children ring the possible result of each event.

Use with
Objective 66
    pages 181–182

Focus
Critical Thinking
    Making Generalizations

Overview
This activity will provide children with an opportunity to think analytically and logically. Children examine events and choose the likely result.

Materials
• 11 red beans, 11 white beans
• box or paper bag
• clear tape

Teaching Suggestions
Tape one red bean and one white bean on the chalkboard. Place 10 red beans and 10 white beans in a box or paper bag. Call on a volunteer to pick a bean from the box or bag. Have children place the beans along the chalkboard ledge near the beans that have been taped to the chalkboard ledge. Ask children which color bean they think will be picked next. Allow children to make guesses and explain their reasoning. Have a second volunteer pick a bean from the box or bag. After the color is named, have that bean placed along the chalkboard ledge according to the appropriate color. Repeat the activity until all the beans have been picked. As the beans are picked, discuss whether more red or white beans show up first.

Direct children's attention to Master 66. Have children look at the story picture at the top of the page and describe what is happening. Then have children look at the two pictures right under these events. Ask children which picture shows what they

think will happen next and why. (Children will most likely say the picture that shows the broken window because a ball hitting a window will usually break it.) Have children describe the second story. Tell them to ring the picture that shows what they think will happen next.

Extension
Have children listen to each of these stories and suggest possible endings. Have them explain their answers. Read aloud the following stories:

Jim's dog loves to "sing" along with the radio by barking loudly. When Jim's mother wants to listen to the radio, she or Jim takes the dog to the basement so he won't hear the radio. One day Jim's mother forgot to take the dog to the basement before she turned on the radio. What happened next? (The dog "sang" along with the radio.)

Laura's favorite flavor of yogurt is strawberry. Her second favorite is vanilla. One day her father decided to surprise her by bringing some strawberry yogurt home. He stopped at the grocery store, but there wasn't any strawberry yogurt. What do you think he will do? (Possible responses: He will buy vanilla yogurt. He will go to another grocery store.)

Notes for Home   Children ring the possible result of each event.

DECISION MAKING

Notes for Home   Children interpret a situation and ring the object that would be most useful in that picture.

Use with
Objective 67
    pages 183–184

Focus
Decision Making

Overview
This activity will provide children with an opportunity to draw conclusions. Children interpret a situation and determine the object that would be most useful in that situation.

Teaching Suggestions
Act out a pantomime by putting toothpaste on a toothbrush and brushing your teeth in front of the class. Ask children to describe what you are doing. Then ask children if this is something that could happen or could not happen in real life. [could happen] Pantomime flying like a bird and ask children to describe what you are doing. Have children tell whether being able to fly is something that could happen or could not happen in real life. [could not happen] Extend the pantomime activity by having volunteers name one thing that could happen and one thing that could not happen in real life.

Direct children's attention to Master 67. Ask children to describe what they see in the first picture in the top row. (a rainy, windy day) Have children identify the two pictures at the right. [umbrella, beach ball] **Questions:** *On a day like the one shown, which object would be most useful to you? Why?* [The umbrella would be most

useful because it protects you from the rain.] Tell children to ring the answer. Have children discuss and identify the pictures in the other rows. Then have children ring the picture at the right that would be most useful. Call on volunteers to explain their answers.

Extension
Distribute magazines, scissors, paste, and paper to the children. Have them fold their papers in half. Ask children to cut out pictures of things that they or someone in their family can use at home. Have children paste those pictures on the left-hand side of their papers. Then ask children to cut out pictures of things that they could use at a different location rather than home. Have children paste those pictures on the right-hand side of their papers. Allow time for children to show and explain their situations.

Name _____

DECISION MAKING

Notes for Home Children interpret a situation and ring the object that would be most useful in that picture.

CRITICAL THINKING

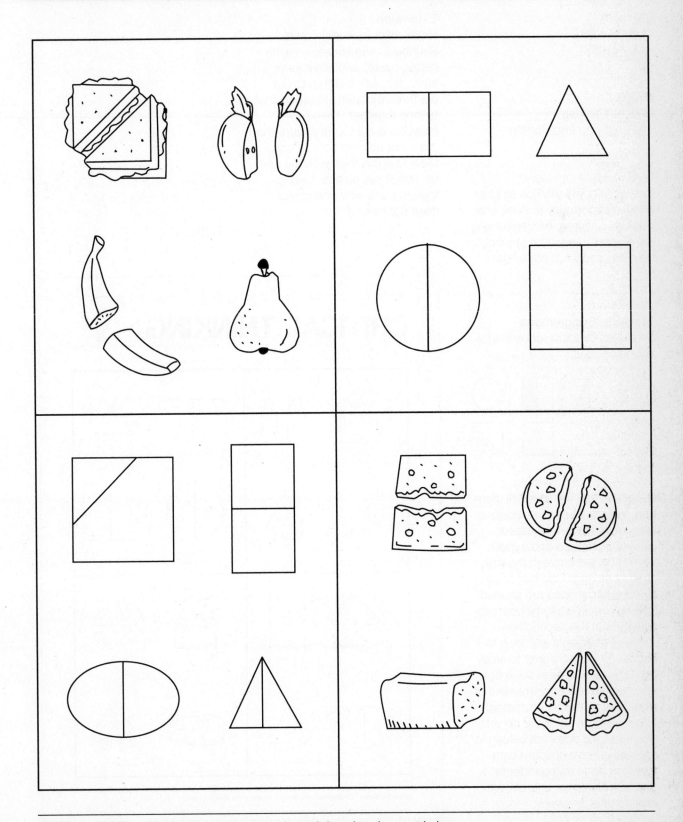

Notes for Home   Children color the object in each box that does not belong.

Teacher Notes

Use with
Objective 68
   page 185

Focus
Critical Thinking
   Classifying and Sorting

Overview
This activity will provide children with an opportunity to think analytically. Children will decide why the objects in each box belong together and what object does not.

Teaching Suggestions
On the chalkboard, draw the following shapes.

Ask children to look at the shapes in the first row. Tell them that one shape does not belong in the row. Have a volunteer identify the shape and explain why. (The last circle in the row doesn't belong. One half of each of the other shapes are shaded. The last circle isn't.) Repeat the activity with the second row.

   Direct children's attention to Master 68. Ask children to study the objects/shapes in each box and decide how they are alike or what they all have in common. Then they can color the object or shape that does not belong in each box. Have children complete the page independently. Call on volunteers to show and explain their answers.

Extension
Have children work in pairs. Distribute magazines, drawing paper, paste, and scissors to each pair. Ask children to cut out three pictures of objects that belong together. Then have them cut out a fourth picture that does **not** belong. Call on volunteers to show their pictures and tell why three objects belong together and why one object does not belong.

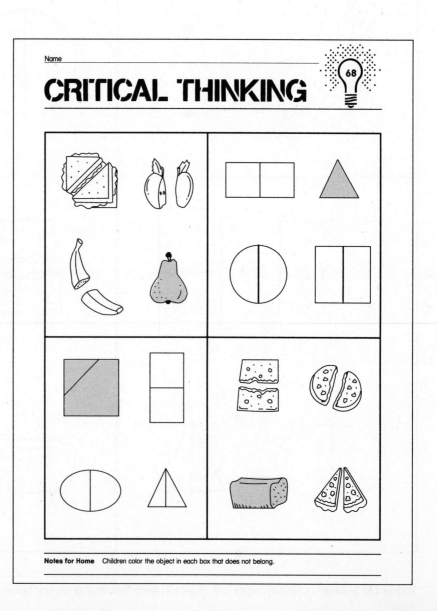

Name _____

CRITICAL THINKING

Notes for Home   Children color the object in each box that does not belong.

DECISION MAKING

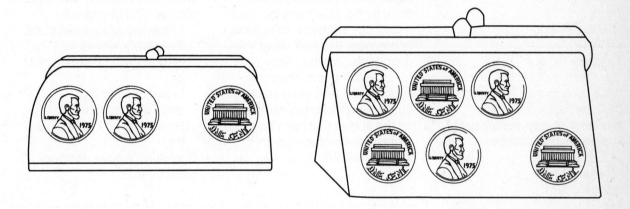

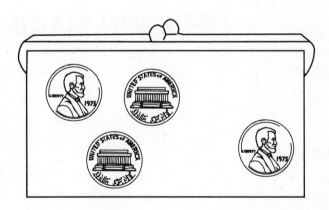

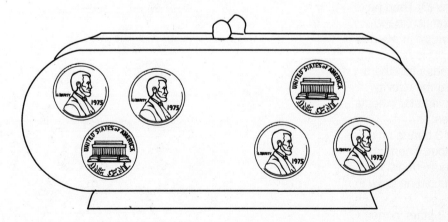

Notes for Home   Children mark an X on the coin purses that hold pennies that total 6¢.

Use with
Objective 69
   pages 195–196

Focus
Decision Making

Overview
This activity will provide children with an opportunity to analyze and think logically. Children mark an X on coin purses holding pennies that total 6¢.

Materials
• flannel board
• felt cutouts of 3 fish, 4 hearts, and 6 stars

Teaching Suggestions
Display the flannel board. Model the following story with felt cutouts of fish as you read it aloud to the children.
   Anna went fishing with her father.
   She caught one fish.
   Later on she caught two more fish.
   How many fish did she catch in all?
Ask children to tell how many fish Anna caught. [3] Then have children count the fish in the story. Write the number of each fish on the board. Have a volunteer write how many fish there are in all. Repeat the activity using the heart and star cutouts with these stories.
   1. Paco drew 3 hearts on a sheet of paper. Then he drew one more heart. How many hearts did he draw in all? [4]
   2. Laura saw 3 stars in the sky. Then she saw 3 more stars in the sky. How many stars did she see all together? [6]

Direct children's attention to Master 69. Have children describe what they see. If they would like to buy a toy at the store for 6¢, how many pennies would they need in a coin purse to purchase this toy? Have children decide whether each coin purse has enough money by counting the pennies in each purse. Tell children to mark an X on the purses that have 6¢ in them. Call on volunteers to explain their answers.

Extension
Give 6 counters to each child. Encourage children to use the counters as they answer questions orally. For example:
   I have two white kittens and three black kittens.
   How many do I have in all? [5]
   I have one red hat and five blue hats.
   How many do I have in all? [6]
Continue for other numbers, sums up to 6.

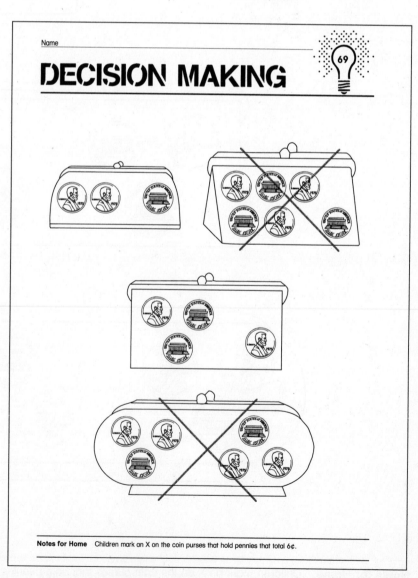

Name _____

DECISION MAKING

Notes for Home   Children mark an X on the coin purses that hold pennies that total 6¢.

CRITICAL THINKING

70

1 + 1	
3 + 1	
1 + 2	
3 + 2	

Notes for Home   Children match by drawing a line from how many to a picture.

Use after pages 197–198.

Use with
Objective 70
    pages 197–198

Focus
Critical Thinking
    Using Logic

Overview
This activity will provide children with an opportunity to think analytically and logically. Children match addition facts to pictures by drawing lines.

Teaching Suggestions
Draw the following on the chalkboard:

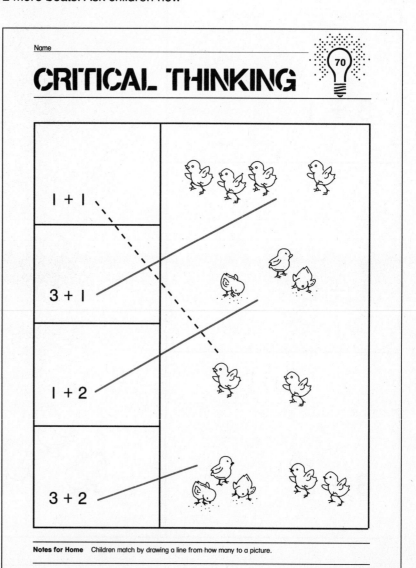

Have children tell about the first picture. (3 children are joining 1 child) Then ask a volunteer to point to the numbers that tell about the picture. [3 + 1] Remind children that the **plus sign** means they should join the figures to find out how many children there are in all. Call on another volunteer to write the number in that box that tells how many children there are in all. [4] Repeat the activity by drawing 4 balls and 1 ball; 5 apples and 1 apple. Call on volunteers to choose the correct numbers and write the answers in the boxes.

   Direct children's attention to Master 70. Have children read the number facts at the left. Ask

children to add the first set of numbers at the left and then draw a line to the picture that shows how many in all. Call on volunteers to explain their answers.

Extension
Use a drum or another rhythm instrument. Tell children to listen as you play 2 beats. Pound the drum two times and have children count with you. Then play 2 more beats. Ask children how

many beats they heard in all. [4] Repeat the activity with other combinations of beats whose sums are 6 or less.

Name _____

CRITICAL THINKING 70

1 + 1	
3 + 1	
1 + 2	
3 + 2	

Notes for Home   Children match by drawing a line from how many to a picture.

VISUAL THINKING

$1 + 1$ 2 $2 + 1$ 3

$3 + 1$ $4 + 1$

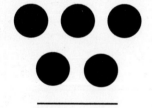 

Use with

Objective 71
    pages 199–200

Focus

Visual Thinking
    Visual Patterns

Overview

This activity will provide children with experience in making judgments. Children identify the addition pattern and supply missing numbers and dots to complete the pattern.

Materials

• 6 blocks

Teaching Suggestions

On a table place 2 blocks together in one group and 2 blocks in another group. Ask children to tell the number of blocks in each group and then how many blocks in all. [2; 4] Write the numbers on the chalkboard: 2 + 2 [4]

Direct children's attention to Master 71. Ask children to count the circles and name the numbers of circles with you in the first row. Ask children what number they should write on the lines under the last picture in the first row. [3] Call on a volunteer to explain why. [There are 3 circles with dots in the middle.] Review the pictures in the row. Explain that each group is 1 more than the last group.

Then explain that the patterns are continued in the next two rows. Have children add and write the numbers to continue the pattern. When children get to the last box in row 2 and 3, ask them what must be done to the circles to finish the pattern. [Add a dot to the middle of each

circle.] Have children add the dots. Explain that the circles with the dots show the sum of each problem.

Extension

Use index cards to write addition exercises with sums to 6. Make five sets. Prepare five sets of number cards 1 to 6. Separate children into 5 groups. Give each group a set of addition exercises and number cards. Mix the sets together. Assign a child to deal an equal amount of cards to each group member.

Have children play a version of "Go Fish" by asking each other for a number card that is the sum of one of their addition cards. If a player gets a match, he or she puts the cards facedown. Each player has one turn at a time. The player who gets the most matching pairs is the winner.

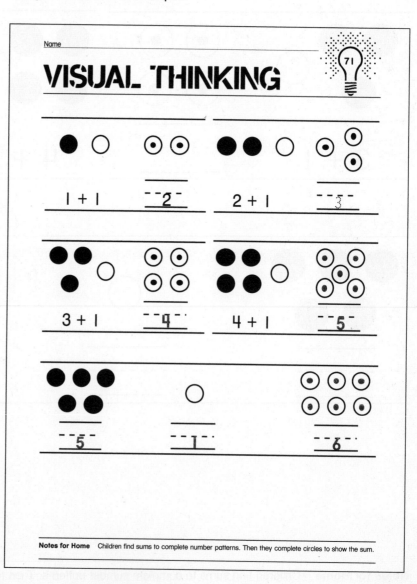

VISUAL THINKING

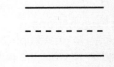 $- - - - + - - - -$ $- - - - -$

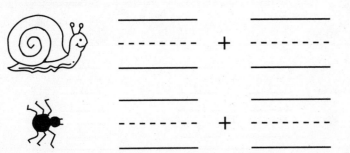 $- - - - + - - - -$ $- - - - -$

$- - - - + - - - -$ $- - - - -$

Notes for Home   Children explore picture stories and add to find how many in all.

Use with

Objective 72
pages 201–202

Focus

Visual Thinking
Spatial Perception

Overview

This activity will provide children with an opportunity to make judgments. Children interpret picture stories and add to find how many in all.

Teaching Suggestions

Ask 2 children to stand up. Call on a volunteer to write the number on the chalkboard that tells how many children are standing. [2] Then ask 3 more children to stand up. Have another volunteer write the number that represents the standing children. [3] Add the plus sign and ask the class to tell how many children in all are now standing. [5] Call on a volunteer to write the number that tells the answer. Repeat the activity with groups of 2 and 4 children; 1 and 3 children.

Direct children's attention to Master 72. Have children look at the first picture story and describe what they see in each box. Ask children how many kites they see in the first picture [1]; how many in the second picture [2]; and how many kites are in the third picture. [3] Tell children to write the numbers under each picture that tells about the kites.

Then have children look at the next picture story and describe it. Children may need help in identifying the snail. Ask chil-

dren how many snails and spiders are in the first picture. [1, 2] Have children tell how many snails and spiders are in the second picture. [none, 1] Finally have the number of snails and spiders in the third picture identified. [1, 3] Have children write the numbers next to the appropriate pictures.

Extension

Have children work in pairs. Distribute magazines, scissors,

drawing paper, paste, and crayons to each pair. Show children how to fold their papers in half vertically. Write these two addition examples on the chalkboard:

$$4 + 2 \qquad 2 + 3$$

Have children copy the addition examples on their papers. Then they can cut and paste objects to show the number story. Then tell children to write the number that tells how many in all.

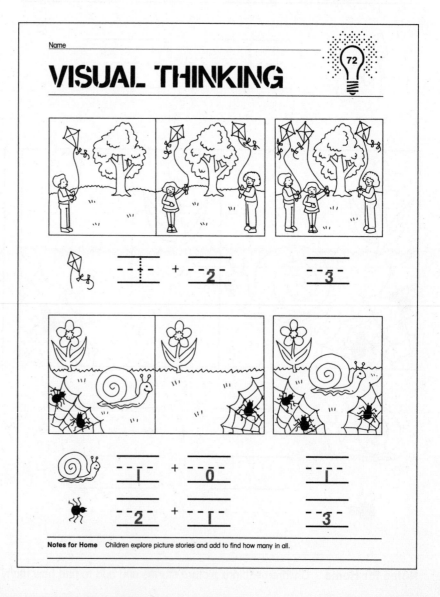

PROBLEM SOLVING

73

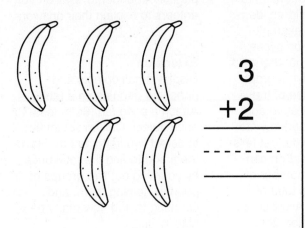

$$3$$
$$+2$$
$$\overline{}$$

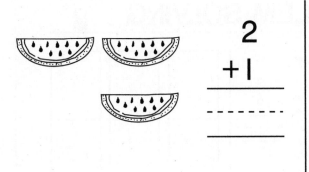

$$2$$
$$+1$$
$$\overline{}$$

$$2$$
$$+2$$
$$\overline{}$$

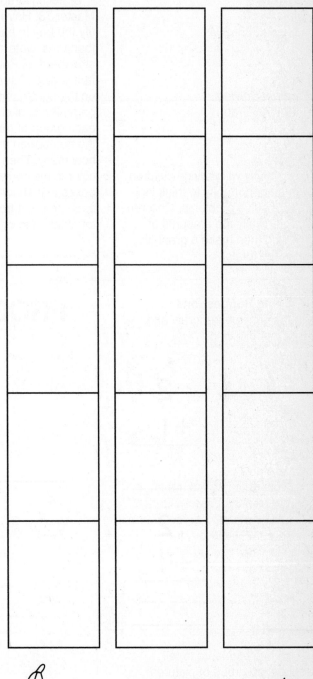

Notes for Home   Children add vertically and then color in a graph to show the totals.

Teacher Notes

Use with
Objective 73
   pages 203–204

Focus
Problem Solving
   Make a Graph

Overview
This activity will provide children with an opportunity to think logically to solve problems. Children add vertically the amounts of fruit and then make a graph to show the totals.

Teaching Suggestions
On the chalkboard, draw and write the following:

    2
    +1
- - - - - - -

⛵⛵   2
⛵⛵⛵⛵   +4
- - - - - - -

Call on volunteers to tell about each group of pictures and numbers. Then have the class add the numbers together. Call on other volunteers to write the numbers that tell how many in all. Repeat the activity as necessary, using other addition examples to 6.

Direct children's attention to Master 73. Have children identify the fruit in each example. [bananas, watermelon slices, strawberries] Point out that each fruit is also pictured in a graph on the right-hand side of the page. First tell children to add each group of fruit and to write the number on the line that tells how many. Then children can color in the correct number of boxes that show the total of each group of fruit. Allow time for children to complete the page independently. Call on volunteers to explain their answers.

Extension
Display small objects and punchout pennies on a table. Attach a price tag (6¢ or less) to each object. Call on volunteers to select two items to buy. Have them add to find the total price by counting out two groups of pennies, joining them, and counting to find how many pennies in all.

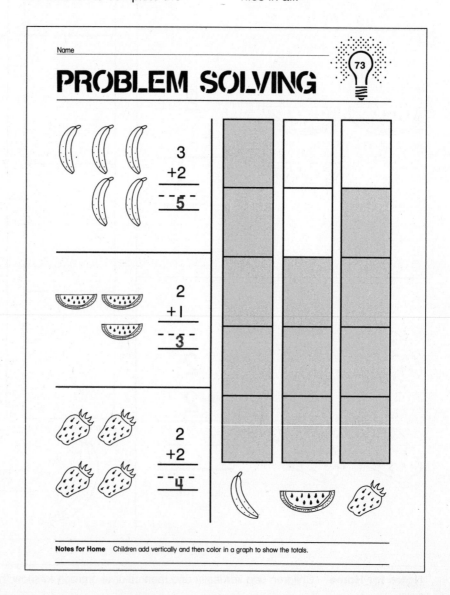

DECISION MAKING

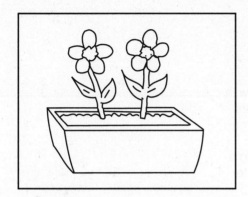

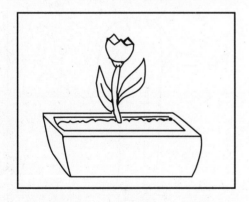

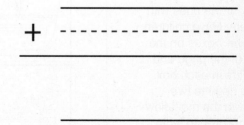

+

74

Notes for Home Children ring the flower boxes that have the most flowers and then add to find how many in all.

  Use after page 205.

Teacher Notes

Use with
Objective 74
  page 205

Focus
Decision Making

Overview
This activity will provide children with an opportunity to draw conclusions. Children find the flower boxes with the most flowers and then add to find the total number of flowers.

Materials
• masking tape
• 6 paper flower cutouts

Teaching Suggestions
Display the paper flower cutouts along the chalkboard ledge. On the chalkboard, write an addition problem in vertical form. Call on a volunteer to tape the right amount of flowers next to each number and to write how many in all. Take the flowers off the chalkboard and repeat the activity with other addition problems in vertical form.

Direct children's attention to Master 74. Explain that the boy wants to buy two flower boxes and is looking for the ones with the most flowers. Have children look at the flower boxes on the left-hand side of the page and count the flowers in each box. Tell children to ring the two flower boxes with the most flowers. Then tell children to write the numbers on the lines that tell how many flowers in each box and how many in all. Have children work independently.

Call on volunteers to show and explain their answers.

Extension
Have children work in small groups. Provide each group with domino tiles in which both sets of dots total to 6. Have children turn the dominoes facedown. Let children take turns picking a domino and adding the dots to find the total.

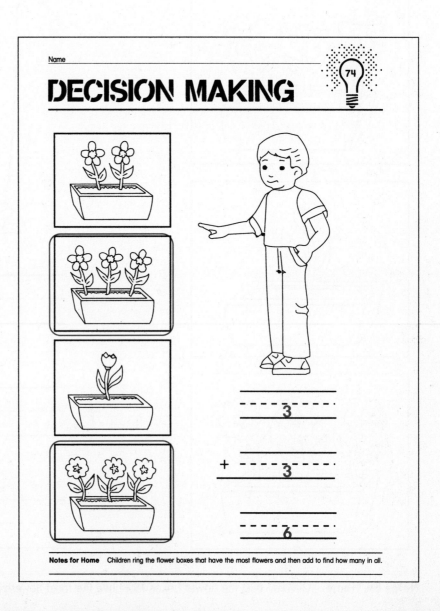

Name _____

DECISION MAKING 74

$$\begin{array}{r} 3 \\ +\ 3 \\ \hline 6 \end{array}$$

Notes for Home   Children ring the flower boxes that have the most flowers and then add to find how many in all.

VISUAL THINKING

75

Notes for Home   Children ring the number of animals that are moving away.

Teacher Notes

Use with
Objective 75
    pages 213–214

Focus
Visual Thinking
    Spatial Perception

Overview
This activity will provide children with an opportunity to make judgments. Children ring the group of animals that are leaving.

Materials
• 6 blocks

Teaching Suggestions
Display 6 blocks. Ask a volunteer to take away 4 blocks. Have the class tell how many are left. [2] Have the volunteer put back the blocks in the group. Continue the activity by asking volunteers to take away different amounts of blocks.

Direct children's attention to Master 75. Have children identify the animals in each row. (ducks, frogs, pigs) Explain that in each row, some animals are moving away. Tell children to ring the animals that are moving. Call on volunteers to tell how many are left in each group.

Extension
Read this rhyme to the children.

    Six little pigeons sat in a line.
    Up in the barn in the warm sunshine.
    Three little pigeons flew down on the ground.
    And ate the crumbs that were lying around.

Ask children to tell how many pigeons left the line. [3] Ask children to tell how many were still sitting in the line. [3] Demonstrate the problem on the board with numbers. (6 – 3   3) Then call on volunteers to dramatize the rhyme.

Repeat the rhyme substituting other number combinations to review subtraction facts from 6.

VISUAL THINKING

76

2   4   1

4   2   6

5   3   2

Notes for Home   Children figure out subtraction stories and ring the number that tells how many are left.

Teacher Notes

Use with
Objective 76
  pages 215–216

Focus
Visual Thinking
  Spatial Perception

Overview
This activity will provide children with an opportunity to make judgments. Children interpret subtraction stories and ring the number that tells how many are left.

Teaching Suggestions
Draw four apples on the chalkboard. Have children count them.

Write the number 4 on the chalkboard. Then cross out 2 apples. Have children tell how many apples are being subtracted. [2] Ask children how many apples are left. [2] Repeat the activity by drawing 6 apples and crossing out 4; 5 apples and crossing out 3, and so on.

Direct children's attention to Master 76. Point out the two pictures at the top of the page. Ask children to describe what is happening in each picture. (There are 3 snowmen. 2 snowmen melt from the hot sun.) Then ask children how many snowmen are left. [1] Have children ring the number that tells how many are left.

Then ask children to look at the pictures in the middle of the

page. Have volunteers describe what is happening in each picture. (Four bubbles are coming out of a bubble pipe. Two bubbles popped.) Have children decide how many bubbles are left and ring the appropriate number.

Let the children do the rest of the page independently. Check each child's activity.

Extension
Assign children to work in groups of 6. Tell each group to role play by being farm animals: pigs, cows, horses, chickens. Have each group work together to make up a subtraction story that tells how the animals get lost, run away, walk away, and so on. Have the groups present their stories to the class. Call on other children to tell how many are left.

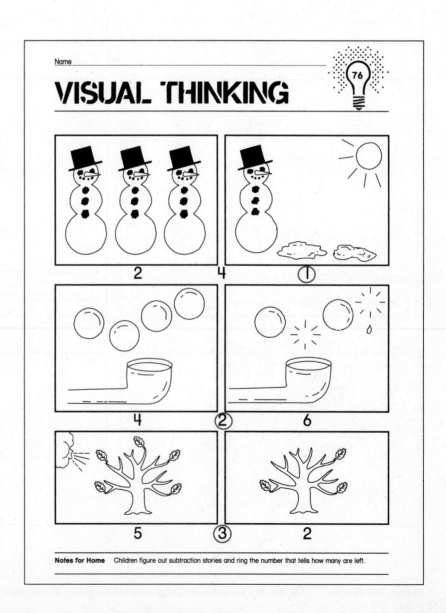

CRITICAL THINKING

77

2 + 1

4 − 2

4 + 1

5 − 1

4 − 3

3 + 2

Notes for Home   Children ring the problem that tells about each subtraction story.

Use with
Objective 77
   pages 217–218

Focus
Critical Thinking
   Using Number Sense

Overview
This activity will provide children with an opportunity to think analytically and logically. Children ring the problem that tells about each subtraction story.

Materials
• 6 toy cars

Teaching Suggestions
Display 6 toy cars. Ask children to count the cars. Move one car away and write the problem 6 – 1 on the chalkboard. Ask children how many cars are left. [5] Provide writing lines on the chalkboard and call on a volunteer to write the number that tells how many are left.

Repeat the activity using a group of 5 cars and taking away 3; 4 cars and taking away 2.

Direct children's attention to Master 77. Have children look at the first picture on the left-hand side of the page. Call on a volunteer to tell about the picture. (Two birds are eating and two birds are flying away.) Then have children look at the problems to the right of the birds. Ask children to ring the problem that tells about the birds. (4 – 2) Call on a volunteer to tell why the other problem is not the answer. (The numbers do not tell about the birds in the pic-

ture. The plus sign means to join together and the birds are going away.) Have children complete the rest of the page independently. Call on volunteers to explain their answers.

Extension
Have children make subtraction mobiles. Distribute a long piece of string or yarn, a pipe cleaner, paper, scissors, and paste to each child. Have children wrap one end of the pipe cleaner around the string or yarn and bend the pipe cleaner so that it is in a perpendicular position. Tell children to draw, cut out, and paste 3 objects on the string and 1 or 2 objects on the pipe cleaner to show the objects being taken away. Let volunteers explain their mobiles.

CRITICAL THINKING

3 − 2 ------- _____

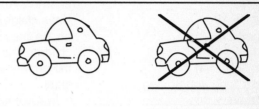

2 − 1 ------- _____

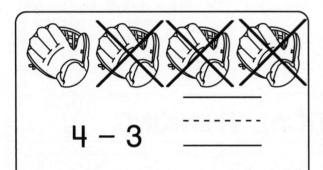

4 − 3 ------- _____

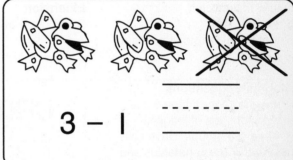

3 − 1 ------- _____

5 − 2 ------- _____

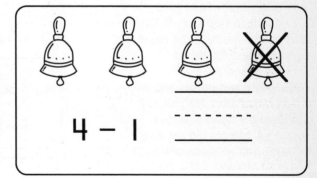

4 − 1 ------- _____

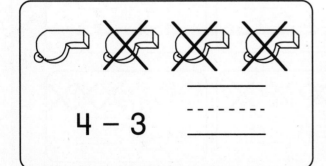

4 − 3 ------- _____

6 − 3 ------- _____

Notes for Home Children write how many objects are left. Then they ring the group of subtraction stories that have the same number of objects left in the boxes.

Teacher Notes

Use with
Objective 78
   pages 219–220

Focus
Critical Thinking
   Classifying and Sorting

Overview
This activity will provide children with an opportunity to think analytically and logically. Children interpret subtraction stories, compare the answers, and ring the stories that have the same number of items left.

Materials
• cutouts of 5 carrots, 4 heads of lettuce
• masking tape

Teaching Suggestions
On the chalkboard, tape 5 carrots and 4 heads of lettuce in two separate groups. Have children identify the vegetables and tell how many of each they see. Write the amount under each vegetable group. Then read aloud the following story to the children. As you read the story aloud, remove the taped amounts indicated.

   Anthony grew carrots and lettuce in his garden. He picked 2 carrots and 1 head of lettuce. How many carrots did he have left? How many heads of lettuce did he have left?

   Have children tell the answers. [3 carrots and 3 heads of lettuce] Call on volunteers to write the answers on the chalkboard: 5 – 2 ___ , 4 – 1 ___ .

   Ask children what is the same about both number stories. (They both have the same amount left.)

   Direct children's attention to Master 78. Have children point to the top-left box. Ask children to read the problems that tell about the picture and to tell the answer of each problem. Have children write the answer on the lines provided. Then tell children that they are to write the answer for each subtraction story.

   When children have completed the number stories, have them ring all the boxes in each half of the page that have the same number of items left. Discuss the answers with the children.

Extension
Distribute drawing paper, crayons, and index cards on which you have written the following subtraction facts:

2 – 1 1, 3 – 1 2, 3 – 2 1,
4 – 1 3, 4 – 2 2, 4 – 3 1,
5 – 1 4, 5 – 2 3, 5 – 3 2,
5 – 4 1, 6 – 1 5, 6 – 2 4,
6 – 3 3, 6 – 4 2, 6 – 5 1.

   Provide a card for each child. Ask children to read the problem and draw a subtraction story about it. Collect the cards and display the pictures. Then hold up the index cards and have children match them to the right picture.

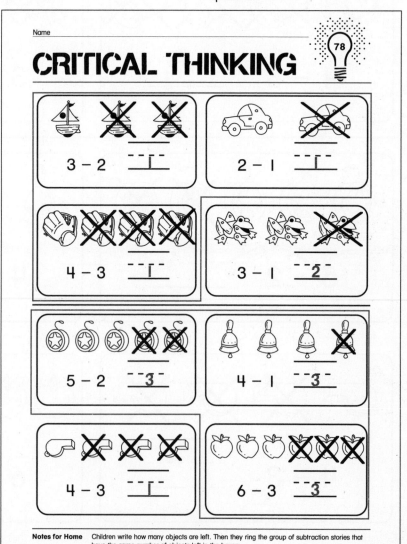

Name _____

CRITICAL THINKING 78

3 – 2 ___1

2 – 1 ___1

4 – 3 ___1

3 – 1 _2_

5 – 2 _3_

4 – 1 _3_

4 – 3 ___1

6 – 3 _3_

Notes for Home Children write how many objects are left. Then they ring the group of subtraction stories that have the same number of objects left in the boxes.

PROBLEM SOLVING

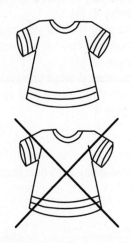

$$\begin{array}{r} 2 \\ -1 \\ \hline \end{array}$$

$$\begin{array}{r} 6 \\ -2 \\ \hline \end{array}$$

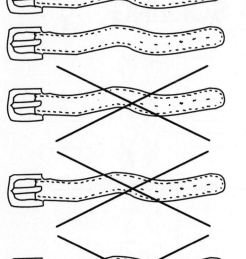

$$\begin{array}{r} 5 \\ -3 \\ \hline \end{array}$$

$$\begin{array}{r} 4 \\ -3 \\ \hline \end{array}$$

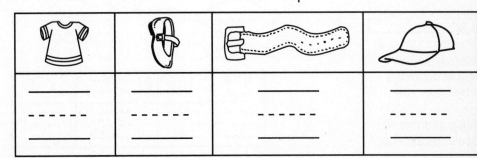

Notes for Home   Children subtract in vertical form. Then they record in the table how many objects are left.

Teacher Notes

Use with
Objective 79
pages 221–222

Focus
Problem Solving
Make a Table

Overview
This activity will provide children with an opportunity to think logically in order to solve problems. Children find answers to subtraction problems and record their answers in a table.

Teaching Suggestions
On the chalkboard draw 4 umbrellas. Put an X on 3 of them. Write the subtraction problem and provide writing lines for children to write the answer. Repeat the activity by drawing 5 leaves and crossing out 4 of them. Now draw a table on the chalkboard to look like the following:

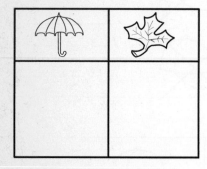

Have volunteers write the number in the table under the correct picture that tells how many are left.

Direct children's attention to Master 79. Discuss each set of clothing with the children. Tell them that after they complete

the subtraction problems they should write the answers in the table. Have children complete the page independently. Check children's work.

Extension
Play a game of "What's My Number?" with the children. Tell children you will give a clue about each number you are thinking of, and they are to guess the number. Use the following clues:

1. This number is what you have left when you have 5 and you take away 4. [1]
2. This number is what you have left when you have 6 and you take away 2. [4]
3. This number is what you have left when you have 3 and you take away 1. [2]

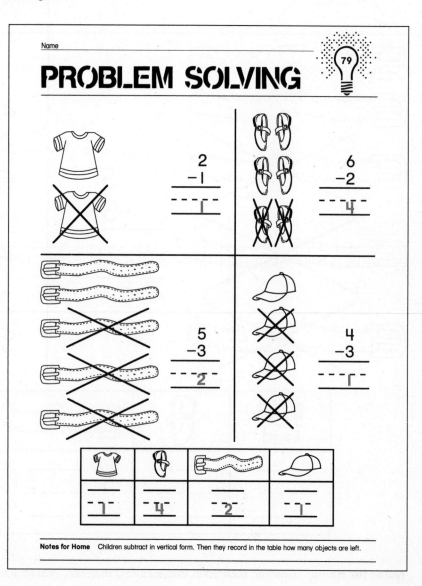

DECISION MAKING

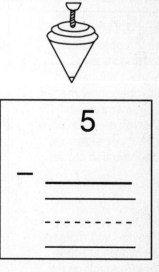

6	5
− _____	− _____
_____	_____
- - - - - -	- - - - - -
_____	_____

Notes for Home   Children decide what objects to give away. Then they complete subtraction problems to match the decision.

Problem Solving and Critical Thinking/**EXPLORING MATHEMATICS** © Scott, Foresman and Company/K   Use after page 223.

Use with

Objective 80
  page 223

Focus

Decision Making

Overview

This activity will provide children with an opportunity to draw conclusions. Children choose objects to give away and write subtraction problems to tell about each decision.

Teaching Suggestions

On the chalkboard draw 4 balloons. Call on a volunteer to make up a story about the 4 balloons and how 2 of them blow away. Have the child draw an X on 2 of them. Write a problem on the chalkboard that tells about the balloon story. Call on a volunteer to tell and write on the chalkboard how many are left. Repeat the activity by drawing 6 fish.

Direct children's attention to Master 80. Explain that the children in the picture are moving away and cannot take all their toys with them. Tell children to draw an X on the objects they would choose to give away. Have them write a subtraction story that tells about how many are being given away and how many are left. Call on volunteers to tell about their decisions and to read their subtraction stories aloud.

Extension

Take the class to a gym or an open area. Provide soft mats for rolling. Have children practice rolling over before teaching this song. Then have groups of six children sing and act out the song.

There were six in the bed and the little one said,
 "Roll over, roll over."
 And they all rolled over and one fell out.
 There were five in the bed and the little one said,
 "Roll over, roll over."
 And they all rolled over and one fell out.
 There were four in the bed and the little one said,
 "Roll over, roll over."
 And they all rolled over and one fell out.

There were three in the bed and the little one said,
 "Roll over, roll over."
 And they all rolled over and one fell out.
 There were two in the bed and the little one said,
 "Roll over, roll over."
 And they all rolled over and one fell out.
 There was one in the bed and the little one said,
 "Good night."

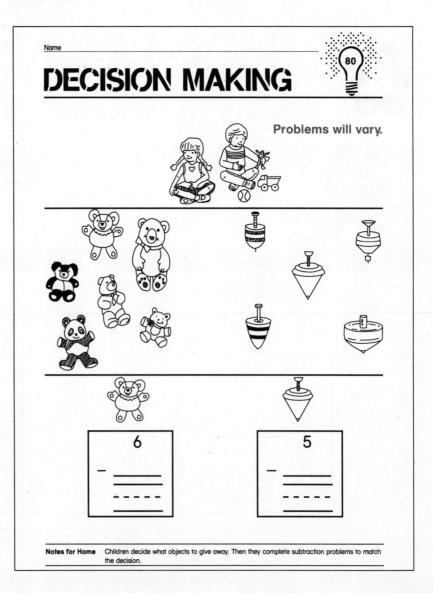

Name _____

DECISION MAKING

Problems will vary.

6

__ __ __ __
__ _ _ _ _

5

__ __ __ __
__ _ _ _ _

Notes for Home   Children decide what objects to give away. Then they complete subtraction problems to match the decision.

VISUAL THINKING

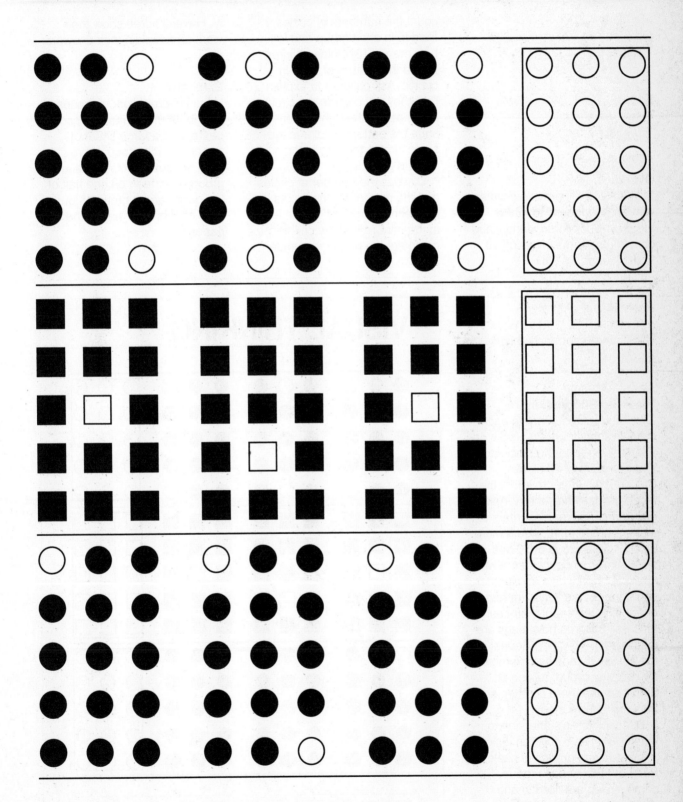

Notes for Home   Children identify and continue patterns involving 13 and 14.

Teacher Notes

Use with

Objective 81
    pages 231–232

Focus

Visual Thinking
    Visual Patterns

Overview

This activity will provide children with an opportunity to make judgments. Children identify and continue patterns involving 13 and 14 items.

Materials

- 14 blocks
- 14 counters for each child
- crayons

Teaching Suggestions

Give fourteen counters to each child. Display fourteen blocks on a table. Separate the blocks to show a group of 10 blocks. Call on a volunteer to count the blocks and tell how many. Ask children to use their counters to make a group of 10. Add 3 more blocks to the group of 10 and ask children to do the same with their counters. Have a volunteer count the blocks while the rest of the children count their counters. Ask children how many are in the group now. [13] Repeat the activity by adding one more block to the group, having children add one more counter, and then telling how many. [14]

Direct children's attention to Master 81. Have children look at the first row of groups of circles. Point out that in each group, some circles are filled in and some are not. Have children

count the numbers of circles filled in in each group and tell how many. [13] Guide children to see the pattern of filled-in circles. Ask children to explain how they will color in the circles in the box at the right to continue the pattern. (Color in the same circles that are in the second group.)

Discuss the number of circles and the pattern for the boxes in the second row and the circles in the third row. Have children complete the page independent-

ly. Have children show their work and explain their answers.

Extension

Have children work in groups. Distribute magazines, scissors, paste, and a large sheet of paper to each group. Have children cut out objects to make a group of thirteen on one half of the paper and a group of fourteen on the other half of the paper.

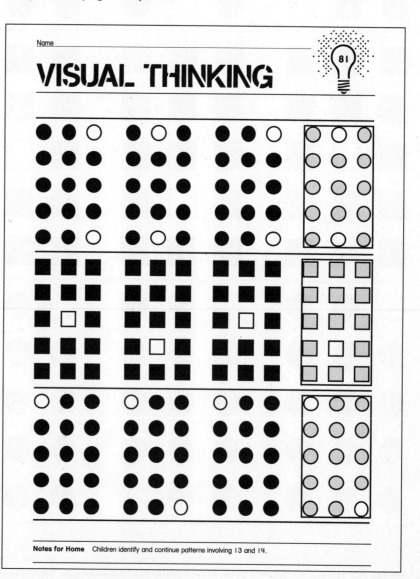

PROBLEM SOLVING

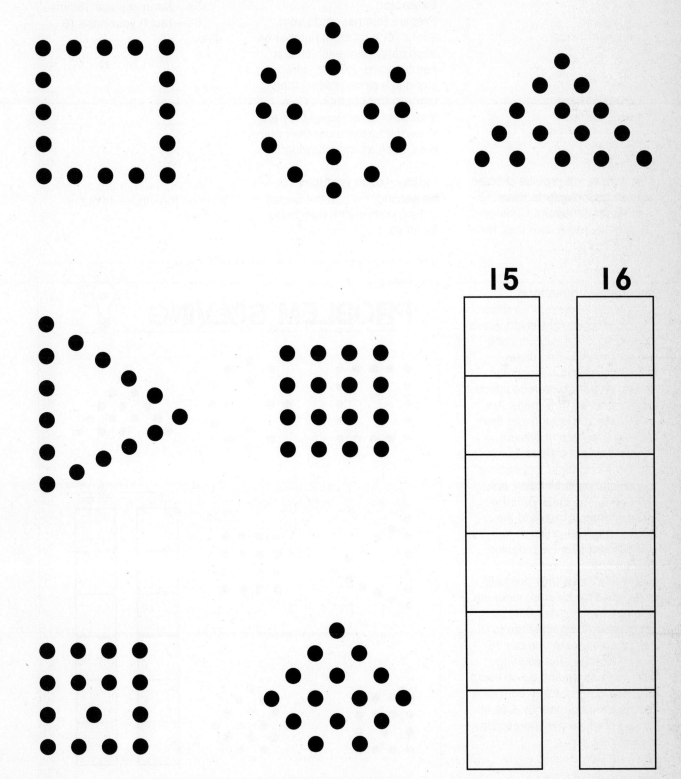

82

15   16

Notes for Home   Children count the designs with 15 dots and 16 dots. Then they record their findings
on a graph.

Use with

Objective 82
   pages 233–234

Focus

Problem Solving
   Make a Graph

Overview

This activity will provide children with an opportunity to think logically and analytically. Children count dots and record their findings on a graph.

Teaching Suggestions

On the chalkboard, draw fifteen circles in a circular design. Have children count the circles and tell how many. Then draw sixteen circles in a triangular design. Have children count the circles and tell how many. Ask children which design has more circles. [the circular design]

Direct children's attention to Master 82. Explain that each of the designs has fifteen or sixteen dots. Then point out the two columns of boxes in the right corner. Tell children to count the dots in each design. Explain that for every design with fifteen dots, they are to fill in a box in the column under the number 15; for every design with sixteen dots, they are to fill in a box under the number 16. Tell children to start coloring from the bottom and go up each column. Have children complete the page independently. Call on volunteers to show and explain their answers.

Extension

Prepare number cards from 13 to 16, a different number on each card. Give each child a number card. Have children stand in a circle holding their cards in front of them. Give directions for activities they are to perform as you call their numbers, such as the following:

   13s—Touch your toes 13 times.
   14s—Wave your right hand 14 times.

   15s—Jump in place 15 times.
   16s—Touch your nose 16 times.

Name _____

PROBLEM SOLVING

Notes for Home   Children count the designs with 15 dots and 16 dots. Then they record their findings on a graph.

VISUAL THINKING

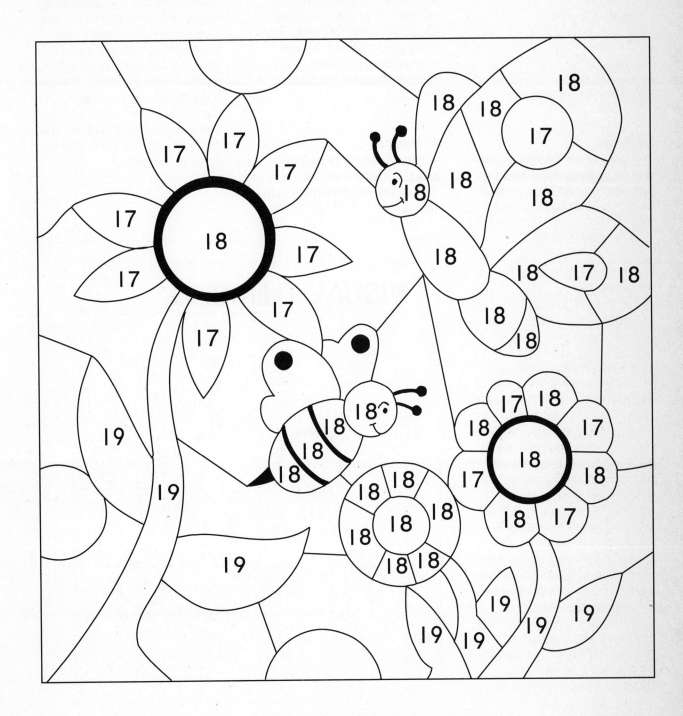

83

Notes for Home Children find a hidden picture by coloring shapes marked 17 with orange, 18 with yellow, and 19 with green.

Teacher Notes

Use with
Objective 83
pages 235–236

Focus
Visual Thinking
  Spatial Perception

Overview
This activity will provide children with an opportunity to analyze and obtain information from pictures. Children color shapes marked with 17, 18, and 19 to reveal a hidden picture.

Materials
• chalk
• crayons

Teaching Suggestions
In an open area, mark a starting line with chalk. Call on a child to take seventeen giant steps from the line. Have the other children count along as the child takes the steps. Have the child remain wherever he or she stops. Call on a second child to take eighteen giant steps from the line. Ask a third child to take nineteen giant steps from the line. With each action, have the other children count along. Then have children compare the positions of the three volunteers.
Questions: Who is the farthest from the starting place? Who is the closest? Which number of steps is the greatest? [19] *Which number of steps is the least?* [17]

  Direct children's attention to Master 83. Point out that there is a hidden picture. Tell children to find all the shapes with the number 17 and color those shapes orange; color shapes marked 18 yellow; and color shapes marked 19 green. Have children complete the page independently. Call on volunteers to describe the picture they see.

Extension
Separate children into small groups. Prepare two sets of 5 index cards each with the numbers 15, 16, 17, 18, and 19 for each group to play a game of "Concentration." Tell children to mix up the cards and turn them facedown. Have players take turns turning over two cards at a time. If a player makes a match, he/she keeps the cards. If there is no match, the cards are placed facedown again and the game continues. The player with the most cards at the end of the game is the winner.

Name _____

VISUAL THINKING

Flowers—Yellow & Orange   Stems—Green
Bee—Yellow   Butterfly—Yellow & Orange

Notes for Home Children find a hidden picture by coloring shapes marked 17 with orange, 18 with yellow, and 19 with green.

CRITICAL THINKING

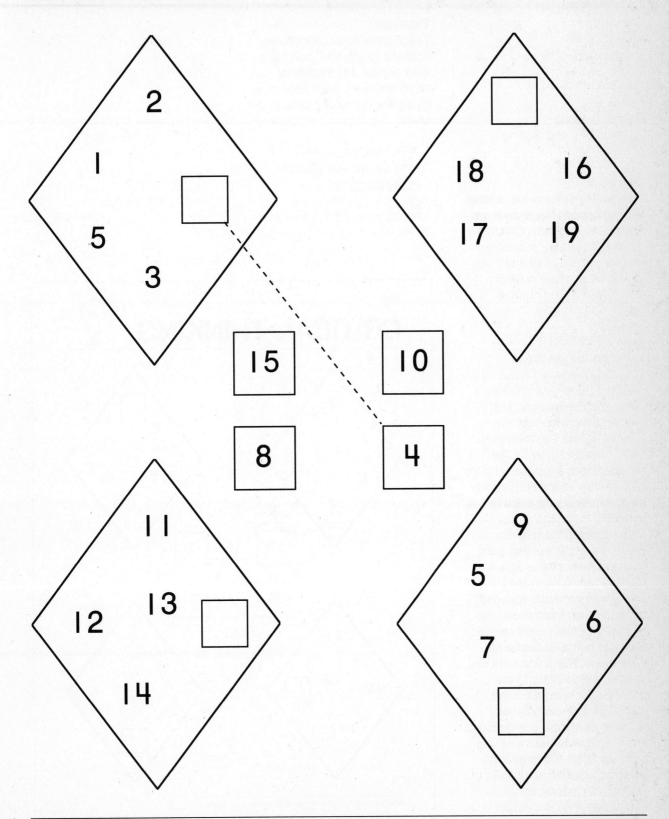

Notes for Home   Children find the missing number in each group.

Problem Solving and Critical Thinking/**EXPLORING MATHEMATICS** © Scott, Foresman and Company/**K**   Use after pages 237–238.

Use with
Objective 84
    pages 237–238

Focus
Critical Thinking
    Classifying and Sorting

Overview
This activity will provide children with an opportunity to think analytically and logically. Children determine how the numbers of each group are alike and then draw lines to show in which group each boxed number belongs.

Teaching Suggestions
Write the numbers 14 and 19 on the chalkboard. Ask children which number is larger. [19] Repeat the activity with the numbers 7 and 11. Then write the numbers 12 and 13. Ask which number is smaller. [12] Repeat once more with another set of numbers and ask which is smaller.

    Direct children's attention to Master 84. Point out that each diamond is missing a boxed number. Tell children to look at the numbers in each diamond and decide on the number that is missing. Each boxed number goes into only one diamond. Have them draw a line from that number in the center to the empty box in each diamond to show where the number belongs. Complete one diamond with the children before having them complete the page independently. Call on volunteers to explain their answers.

Extension
Teach children to count by 2s from 0 through 10. Then have them repeat this traditional cheer with you, each time supplying the name of a child in the class.

    Two, four, six, eight—
    Who do we appreciate?
     (Child's name)   !

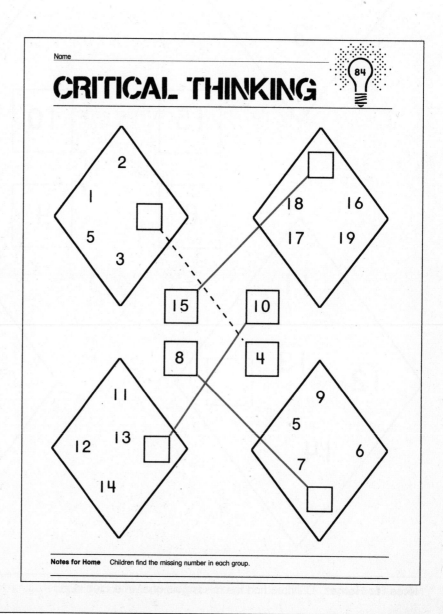

Children find the missing number in each group.

DECISION MAKING

Notes for Home Children choose 5 animals and write their numbers in order.

Problem Solving and Critical Thinking/**EXPLORING MATHEMATICS** © Scott, Foresman and Company/**K**   Use after pages 239–240.

Teacher Notes

Use with
Objective 85
    pages 239–240

Focus
Decision Making

Overview
This activity will provide children with an opportunity to draw conclusions. Children choose five numbered animals and arrange the five numbers in increasing order.

Materials
• number line 1 through 19

Teaching Suggestions
Prepare and display a number line from 1 through 19. Have children count from 1 through 19 as you point to the numbers. **Questions:** *What number comes after 18?* [19] *What comes before 12?* [11] *What comes between 15 and 17?* [16]

   Direct children's attention to Master 85. Have the animals and numbers identified. Explain that a new zoo is opening and the director of the zoo wants to choose 5 animals to appear on a poster about the zoo. Tell children to ring the 5 animals that they would like to see on a poster. Then have them write the numbers of those animals on the lines at the bottom of the page. Explain that the numbers should be written in order from the smallest number to the largest. Call on volunteers to tell their choices and explain their reasons.

Extension
Distribute number cards 1 through 19 to nineteen children. Have the children arrange themselves according to the card in numerical order. The children then can count out loud. Collect the cards, shuffle them, and repeat the activity. To vary the activity, call on a volunteer to direct the other children in lining up in order.

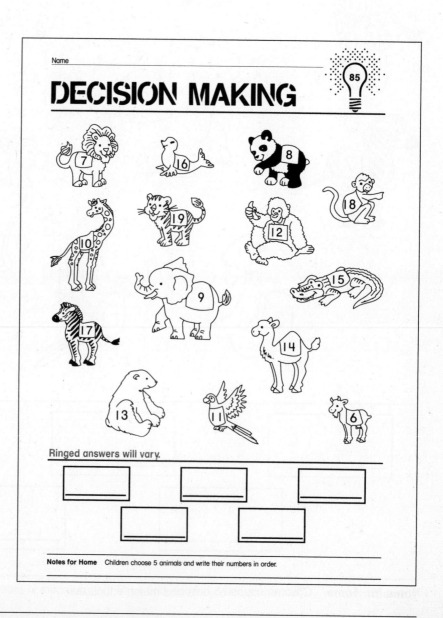

Name

DECISION MAKING

Ringed answers will vary.

Notes for Home   Children choose 5 animals and write their numbers in order.

VISUAL THINKING

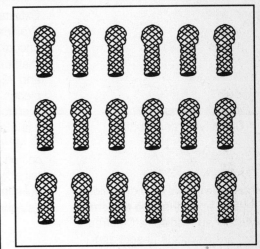

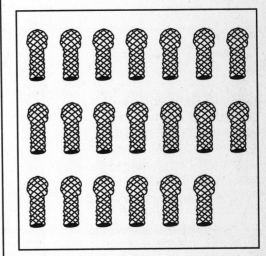

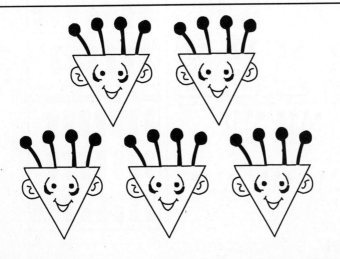

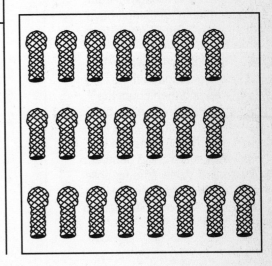

Notes for Home Children count objects and match equal sets.

Teacher Notes

Use with
Objective 86
pages 241–242

Focus
Critical Thinking
Classifying and Sorting

Overview
This activity will provide children with an opportunity to think analytically and logically. Children count the objects in sets and match equal sets.

Materials
• 22 counters for each child

Teaching Suggestions
Distribute 22 counters to each child. Write 20 on the chalkboard and have the number read aloud. Tell children to show that amount with their counters. Repeat the activity by writing the numbers 22, 18, and 21.

Direct children's attention to Master 86. Explain that the three groups of creatures from another planet on the left have ordered antenna warmers from a store, but the orders have gotten mixed up. Ask children to count the antennae on the creatures and then count the antenna warmers in each box. Tell children to draw a line from each group of creatures to the box with the matching number of warmers. Allow time for children to complete the page independently. Call on volunteers to explain their answers.

Extension
Provide an assortment of uncooked beans and macaroni. Distribute paste, drawing paper, and 22 beans or macaroni pieces to each child. Tell children to make a picture or design using all their beans or macaroni. When children have finished, call on volunteers to show and tell about their pictures. Make a bulletin board display with the designs.

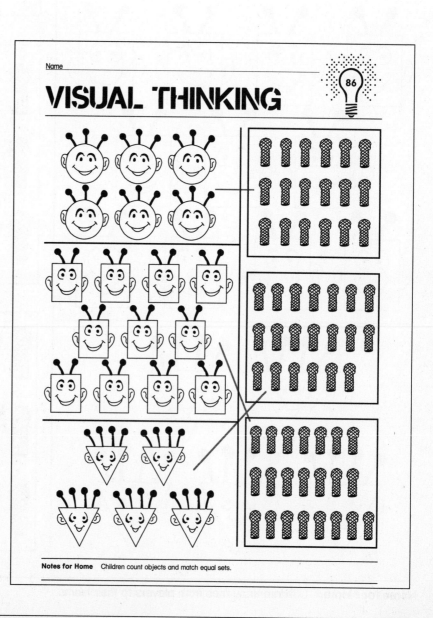

CRITICAL THINKING

87

Notes for Home   Children draw lines from players to their teams.

Teacher Notes

Use with
Objective 87
    pages 243–244

Focus
Critical Thinking
    Classifying and Sorting

Overview
This activity will provide children with an opportunity to use logical reasoning. Children match the children to the appropriate team.

Materials
• number cards 20-25

Teaching Suggestions
Display the number cards along the chalkboard ledge. Have a volunteer select a number card. Ask the class to tell the number. Call on three volunteers to show that number by drawing dots on the chalkboard. Repeat the activity and ask 3 other volunteers to show the amount on the chalkboard.

Direct children's attention to Master 87. Identify the numbers shown on the children at the left. Explain that these children need to find their other team members. Help children identify the number patterns shown on the team members at the left. Have them decide on the number that would complete each group and then draw a line from that child on the left to the appropriate team. Call on volunteers to explain their answers.

Extension
Distribute paste and thirty different colored construction paper strips to each child. Demonstrate how to paste the ends of one strip together to form a loop; then how to form connecting loops to make a chain. Ask each child to make a chain of twenty-three, twenty-four, or twenty-five loops.

When children have finished their chains, have each child show and tell how many loops are on his or her chain. You may wish to join all the chains together to make one very long chain to use as a classroom decoration.

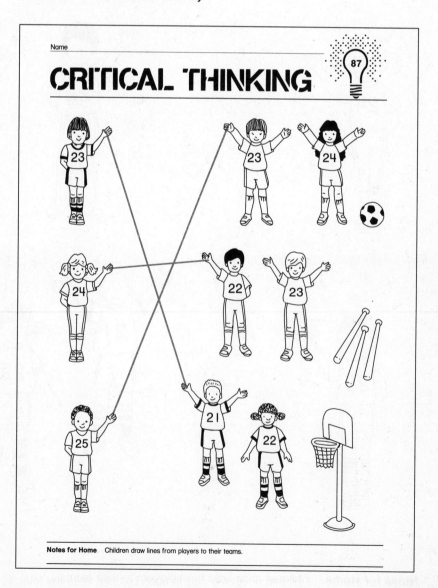

Name

CRITICAL THINKING

87

23   23   24

24   22   23

25   21   22

Notes for Home   Children draw lines from players to their teams.

PROBLEM SOLVING

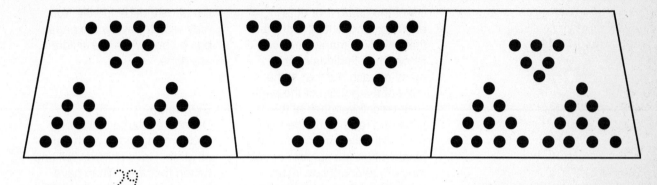

88

29 _____   _____   _____

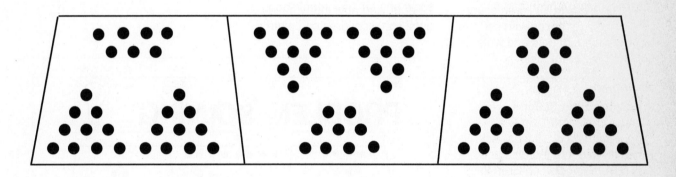

_____   _____   _____

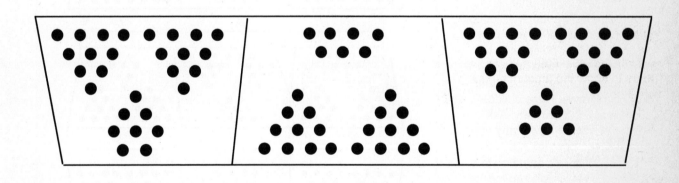

_____   _____   _____

26 ●	27 ●	28 ●	29 ●

Notes for Home   Children count the dots in each box and write the totals for each amount in the table.

Use with
Objective 88
    pages 245–246

Focus
Problem Solving
    Make a Table

Overview
This activity will provide children with an opportunity to think visually and logically. Children count the number of boxes with certain numbers of dots and write their findings in a table.

Teaching Suggestions
On the chalkboard, draw a triangular shape of 10 dots. Ask children to count the dots and tell how many. Ask children to name the shape of the arrangement of dots. [triangle] Then draw the same triangular arrangement of another 10 dots. Have children look at your new drawing and see if they can tell how many dots there are without counting. Then add another 8 dots in 2 rows. Have children count and tell how many. Ask children to count how many dots there are all together. [28]

Direct children's attention to Master 88. Have children look at the first box with the three groups of dots. Have children count the dots and tell how many in all. [29] Tell children to write the number on the lines below the box. Then point out the other boxes with dots. Guide children to see that each box has some similar designs of triangles of 10 dots and then some other shapes with less dots. Explain that children will

count the number of dots in each box and write the number that tells how many. They will record their findings of how many of each number in the table at the bottom of the page.

Have children look at the table and read aloud the numbers. Tell children that after they have written the number of dots, they are to count how many boxes have 26 dots, how many have 27 dots, how many have 28 dots, and how many have 29 dots. Have children complete

the page independently. You may wish to review the page box by box when the children are done.

Extension
Distribute a large ball of clay and a rolling pin to each pair of children. Have children roll and flatten their clay. Then have them make numbers 26 to 29 with their clay.

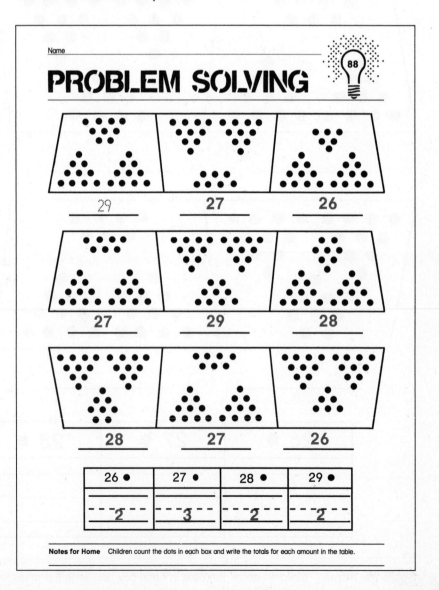

PROBLEM SOLVING

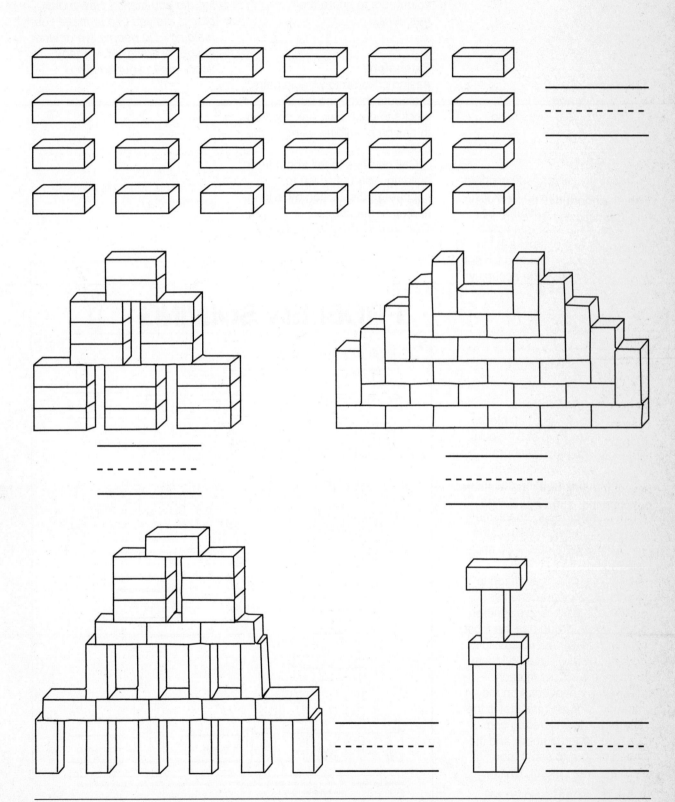

89

Notes for Home Children guess and ring the picture that has the most blocks. Then they count the blocks to see if they are right.

Use with
Objective 89
 pages 247–248

Focus
Problem Solving
 Using Logical Reasoning

Overview
This activity will provide children with an opportunity to think visually and logically. Children use visual clues to estimate which pictured group of blocks is the largest, and then count each set of blocks to check the accuracy of the estimate.

Materials
• blocks

Teaching Suggestions
Display one group of 20 blocks and another group of 31 blocks. Show the blocks in random arrangements. Ask children which group they think has more blocks. Then have volunteers count each group to check the children's guesses. Repeat the activity using groups of 30 and 17; 28 and 15.
 Direct children's attention to Master 89. Point out the five groups of blocks. Have children guess which group has the most blocks and, without discussion, *ring that picture*. Then tell them to count the blocks in each group, write each total on the line, and *ring the total* that is the greatest. Ask children to compare the ringed number and the ringed picture to see if their estimate was correct. Call on

volunteers to share their reactions.

Extension
Assign children to work in pairs. Distribute thirty-one building blocks to each pair. Ask children to design a building using all the blocks.
 Call on pairs to tell about their building. You may wish to encourage discussion by asking each pair questions.
Questions: *What kind of build-*

ing did you make? How many blocks did you use to make your building? Do people live or work in your building? How many floors are in your building?

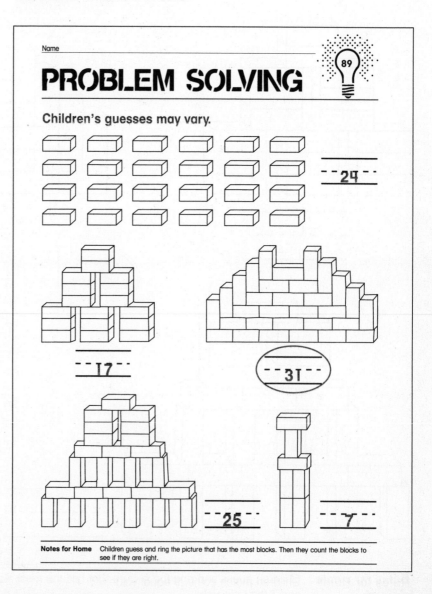

CRITICAL THINKING

Notes for Home   Children match coins of equal value.

Use with
Objective 90
    pages 249–250

Focus
Critical Thinking
    Classifying and Sorting

Overview
This activity will provide children with an opportunity to think analytically and logically. Children determine the value of pictured coins and match them to other coins of equal value.

Materials
• punchout pennies, nickels, dimes, and a quarter

Teaching Suggestions
Display the punchout money on a table. Hold up 3 punchout pennies and ask children to count the pennies. [3¢] Then hold up 5 pennies and have children identify the money amount. [5¢] Call on a volunteer to find another coin on the table that has the same value as the pennies. Repeat the activity with 2 nickels, having children find another coin that has the same value. Then hold up the quarter. Ask children to name the coin. Let volunteers try to pick out other coins that total the same amount.

   Direct children's attention to Master 90. Have children identify the coins. Tell children to match the groups of coins on the left to those on the right that are worth the same amount. Have children work independently. Call on volunteers to

explain their answers. If children have difficulty, review the page using the punchout coins.

Extension
Separate the children into groups. Give each group punchout pennies, nickels, dimes and a quarter. Have each group together decide on a specific amount to show. Let others in the class name that amount.

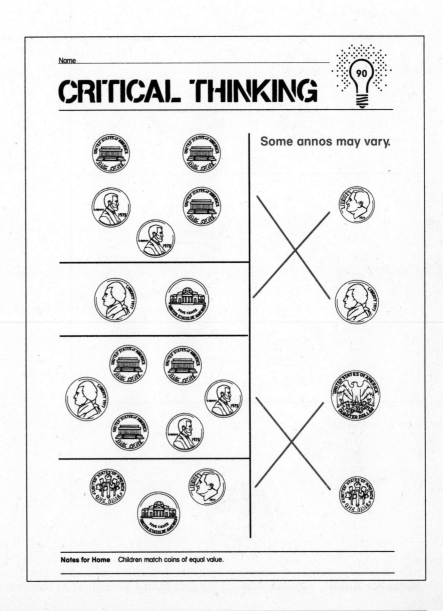

Name _____

CRITICAL THINKING   90

Some annos may vary.

Notes for Home   Children match coins of equal value.

VISUAL THINKING

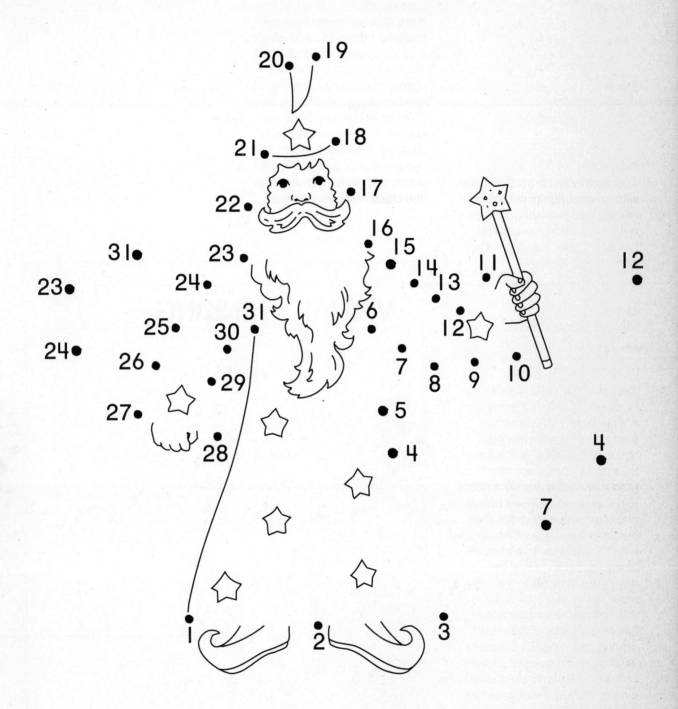

Notes for Home   Children connect the dots from 1 through 31 to complete a picture.

Use with
Objective 91
   page 251

Focus
Visual Thinking
   Spatial Perception

Overview
This activity will provide children with an opportunity to analyze and get information from pictures. Children connect dots numbered from 1 through 31 to complete a picture.

Materials
• number cards 1 to 31

Teaching Suggestions
Place number cards 1 to 31 along the chalkboard ledge in random order. Call on volunteers, in turn, to choose one card each time and place it in sequential order. Begin the activity by finding the number card 1 and placing it in another part of the ledge. Call on a volunteer to find the number card that would follow in sequential order. Continue until all the cards are arranged in numerical order.

   Direct children's attention to Master 91. Discuss the page with the children. Ask children to point to the dot with the number 1 next to it. Explain that the last number in the dot-to-dot picture is 31. Have children complete the page independently by connecting the dots in sequential order. Call on volunteers to show their completed pictures. Have children identify the dot-to-dot picture.

Extension
Have children make their own counting books. Give 31 sheets of drawing paper to each child. Tell children to number the sheets from 1 to 31, writing one number at the top of each page. Then have children draw objects, shapes, and so on to show each number. When children have finished, use a hole punch and yarn to fasten each book together.

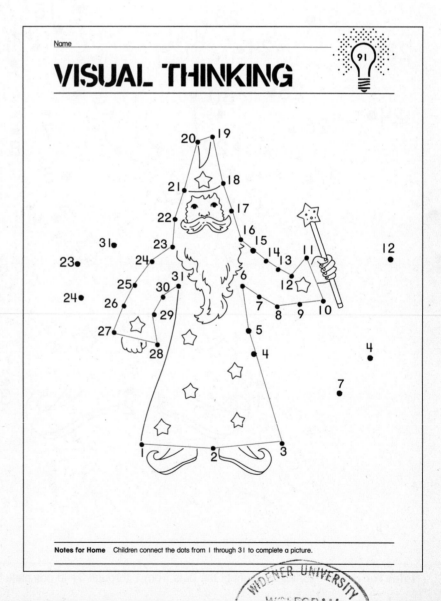

Name

VISUAL THINKING

Notes for Home   Children connect the dots from 1 through 31 to complete a picture.